.... a fresh and insightful commentary (humor, sharp intellect, and a steadfast (the experiences of autistic individuals a including those with profound autism— advice and tackles today's thorniest issu supposed to be able to write is a must-read for anyone eager to understand autism better. As a rising star in the field, Partlow is poised to become this generation's Temple Grandin.

     –Erin R. Hahn, Ph.D.,
     Department Chair and Professor of Psychology, Furman University

---

....unique perspective... as an individual who provides services to individuals with autism and who also has autism herself. Her insights provide both a common sense approach and reveal a wisdom well beyond her years. Her analogies and practical recommendations should be read by... all healthcare workers serving those with autism....

     –Steven A. Skinner, M.D.,
     President and CEO of the Greenwood Genetic Center

I am a mom of an autistic child. [Partlow's] life experiences as an individual on the spectrum as well as a RBT who works directly with autistic clients offer a unique insight and allow readers to feel what it's like to be "on both sides of a bridge." Her brutal honesty and sense of humor shine beautifully through her words!

     –Cara Cobb

From a history in family counseling, I know *everyone* is going to want to get their hands on this book. Analysis from a unique perspective... for parents and clinicians alike. Partlow's view is unlike any other and within these pages she has many lessons to teach us all. You will want to hear what she has to say!

     —Amanda J. Gerding, LMSW,
     Clinical Social Work Therapist and CEO of Lillys Counseling

Life on the Bridge

linking my world to yours
as an autistic therapist

by Kaelynn Partlow,
Registered Behavior Technician

To Mom

and Uncle Tommy

with my thanks to Project Hope Foundation

and my heartfelt best wishes

to autistic people and their loved ones

throughout the world

Contents

Part 1: Framing Our Bridge

Airline cabins seem a strange place to consider bridges, but today that's what's happening. Settling in for a flight, I'm thinking of barriers in our routes and bridges over them. Common destinations with different travel plans. Because of my autism, flying often overwhelms me with sensory input and disruption of routine. But on this trip I'm flying first class for the first time, on my way to talk to an audience of service providers from my personal and clinical experience as an autistic autism professional.

Flying first class adds a new perspective. So much more physical space! Apple juice in hand before the wheels go up. Fewer people. Better food. Softer seats. A long list of benefits creates a simpler, easier trip. While I relax in a cushy seat, I'm considering the fact that many people have never flown any other way. A second fact? An even larger number never will. These realities and truths are far apart, but I wonder if I'm the only human on the plane thinking about why.

First class costs a lot more money, obviously a big factor for most of the world's population. First class also has fewer seats available. Finances aside, time, schedule, and availability play roles. If someone is flying coach, it's not a given they can't afford first class. Maybe they found out only three hours ago that a relative is dying, and they're taking the fastest route, whatever it happens to be.

Several miles below me, other people might be making the same journey by car. Are we all going to Philadelphia? Apparently so. Are those down there on the road driving because they can't afford even the regular air fare? Or are they doing so because they like the scenery, the schedule flexibility, and the autonomy of deciding more details about the travel plan? Because they want to travel with their dogs? Or because they're afraid of planes? Obviously, I'll never know all the factors.

Why am *I* in first class today? A software glitch plopped me here when I didn't plan on it. Random chance changed everything, making my current reality very different from those traveling seven feet behind me—or seven miles below.

Autism isn't so different from long-distance travel. Are we all doing life's journey? Sure. But how and why are subject to vast variation, some within our control, some not. I am coming to you from my life on a bridge, situated between groups with widely varied needs. I'd like to coax you to better understand autism through that framework: myriads of factors, unknown causes, broad divisions, and individual differences. And I'd like to help you bridge the gaps between.

Chapter 1

My Journey

According to the clinicians who diagnosed me, I was never going to read a book, forget writing one. My mother knew I was different starting at a very early age. I've always struggled with keeping friends, tolerating change, and sorting through sensory input. My mom brought up concerns about autism to the pediatricians, but I like to joke that in the 90s, girls couldn't catch autism, which is why I was diagnosed later in childhood. My list of academic challenges grew so long that when I was 10, my uncle paid for extensive academic and psychological testing, resulting in a lengthy list of diagnoses, including autism and various learning disabilities.

Fate has a great sense of humor. My birthday happens to be on April 2. If you're synched with the autism community, you probably recognize that date as World Awareness, World Acceptance, World Fill-in-the-blank-with-the-proper-word Autism Day. The year I was diagnosed with autism? 2007 ... the very year World [insert preferred term] Autism Day was established. My position as an autism advocate sometimes seemed a bit inevitable—a lifelong journey across bridges between contradictory gaps.

- I didn't read my first book independently until I was 14, but by age 27 I was writing one.

- I can't do math beyond a third-grade level, which helped prevent me from attending college. But I frequently speak to college faculty about how to help their students.

- I was diagnosed as a child, and now I work as a therapist delivering autism services to other children.

- I am language abled but spend time each week with those who are severely language challenged.

- I live with neurotypical roommates and have a full-time job, but I require support to know how to pay my bills and manage my schedule.

- I can dress up in an evening gown and present to a ballroom full of people—and I can have head-banging meltdowns in my closet.

- I reach millions of people through my social media, but I have very few personal friends.

- I was fortunate enough to have my life revolutionized by Project Hope Foundation, and now I work for them, trying to mirror that magic for others.

Others might marvel at these broad gaps, but I try to create routes across them. I've come to realize I am not stuck in any of these groups. I can travel between the worlds. My goal in writing this book is to help others also "bridge the gaps."

Probably the most significant bridge I ever crossed happened at age 13 when I joined Project Hope Foundation's school for kids on the autism spectrum. With their encouragement, I soon became a peer mentor, discovering I could interact well with children, especially those on the spectrum. Project Hope's responsiveness to individual needs and preferences meant they developed an internship for me to work towards various goals in helping the teachers.

After receiving my high school diploma, I began more formal training and became certified as a Registered Behavior Technician, qualified to provide therapy in clinical settings. I've been on staff with Project Hope since age 18. My clinical experience is wide, ranging from teaching individuals who use a device to communicate basic needs to those who are refining their ability to engage their peers in discussions of Star Wars. I've provided community, home, and clinical support for clients with extensive histories of dangerous behavior, and I've worked with adults on higher level social and executive functioning skills. I've worked with clients as young as three and as old as 20.

In 2022, I had the opportunity to participate in the Netflix series *Love On the Spectrum*. That experience opened several doors for me, but, unfortunately, none of those doors had a boyfriend behind them. That said, one of those "open doors" led to the expansion—really, the explosion—of my social media reach. Before Netflix, I had a decently large following on Facebook. After Netflix, I quickly realized I needed to expand content beyond fun memes into more substance. I've dedicated my entire social media presence to giving the most authentic autism and behavior analytic information any single individual could hope to portray. After several years of trying to package actionable information into 60-second formats, I decided to compile some of my life-on-the-bridge learnings into a book format, hoping to make the content more accessible to those of you who are interested.

If you've taken the trouble to start this book, you probably already know autism is a spectrum—a broad one. If you are the one on the spectrum or care about someone on the spectrum, you may know quite a bit about that particular place on the spectrum. But are you willing to take the next step?

The complexities of autism create a broad variance of perspectives— from individuals to families to professionals and also to the public. I've dedicated my life and career to creating bridges of understanding among those groups. I want to maneuver on the bridge to build some broader understanding for all. I want each to understand the others to enhance quality of life and everyone's ability to find solutions for challenges. To make that happen, we're going to need to do a deeper dive into what autism is … and what it's not.

Chapter 2

What Autism Is Not

If you haven't already done the requisite internet search for "what is autism," let's save some time. Here's the short answer. Autism is a complex neurodevelopmental condition. That means it's *not* any of the following:

- bad parenting,

- poor self-discipline,

- a personality disorder, or

- a trauma response.

While certain corners of the internet might have you believe that autism is just a set of personality quirks, I can assure you that's far from the truth. Online content creators, myself included, have an incentive to show you, the viewer, the most relatable struggles and differences. Having a reason to show a watered-down version of reality doesn't inherently mean all online content surrounding autism is not genuine. When a toddler asks for apple juice, and you fill the cup with 65% juice and 35% water, you still give them juice—you just dilute what they get.

I don't want to water down your juice unnecessarily, since, if you're reading this book, I have to assume you truly want a better understanding of autism. So my responsibility is to give you what you actually need rather than what you might like to hear. That starts with a realistic understanding of the condition itself. To get there, you'll need to keep a core concept in mind. *No simple list of answers exists.* Neurology is complex; therefore, so is autism. An accurate understanding of autism will always juggle degrees of affect, symptoms, and ability—exactly why we call it a spectrum. From principles of therapy to mere definitions of terms, there's almost nothing on which everyone agrees. We'll circle back to the variations shortly, but first a few more entries for the "not" side of our list—from my perspective, at least.

Lost Car Keys: not invisible

"I can't find my car keys, so they are invisible," said no one, ever! When we can't find something, it's because we don't know where to look, not because the thing has magically become invisible. The same principle applies to autism. Just because you can't see my disability doesn't mean it's invisible. My autism *is* visible to those who know what to look for. But—not so different from the lost car keys—if you don't know where to look, you may not find it at first glance.

All disabilities *are* visible to those who experience them, even if an untrained eye doesn't immediately recognize an issue. Professionals who treat disabilities can certainly see them. Believe me, no disabilities are invisible to the people who have them. They're an intrinsic part of our lives, daily factors that affect every action, making up a crucial portion of who we are. That's the absolute opposite of invisible!

Wishful Thinking: not a superpower

It's common, especially online, to hear people say that autism is a superpower. I consider the statement misleading and problematic. It carries a built-in assumption that all autistic people have superhuman savant skills. While a few may have those skills, 90% do not. The genius stereotype harms valid understanding because it misrepresents what most autistic people are like. A common saying is that if you've met an autistic person, you've met *one* autistic person. We're all incredibly different from each other. Saying that autism is a superpower ignores the individuality that's basic to the autism spectrum. The phrase dismisses the fact that autistic people face countless challenges because of their condition.

As an example, from my experience, yes, I am in a unique position in that being autistic is an advantage in my work as a therapist and an advocate. I believe my autism helps me connect with my clients and powerfully advocate for others. However, saying "autism is a superpower" is far too big of a generalization. That's just not how most people experience their condition. This is one of those things that comes down to opinion and experience, and, of course, that'll vary for each person. So hear me, please, that I'm not saying autism never has its perks, because it absolutely does. But usually, in my own opinion, describing it as a superpower simply doesn't do our stories justice. If you wouldn't say a particular phrase about any other group of people, you probably shouldn't say it about autistic people.

In Need of Life Jackets: not "just a little difference"

"Autism isn't a disability, it's just a little difference." I can't tell you how much that statement makes me want to scream in frustration. From my perspective, we all get thrown into the pool of life. Some people, maybe the majority, figure it out and get to the side without drowning. They may sputter for breath, they may have unorthodox form, but they make it. They may swim a little differently than those who benefit from a swim team coach, but they will survive. Some of us, however, despite our best efforts, will simply sink to the bottom. We can't conjure up a different stroke on our own. We require life jackets to give us, you know, *life*!

Despite hearing this phrase for years, I still can't understand the mindset. Far too many people, autistic and neurotypical, actually *are* out there claiming over and over that "Autism isn't a disorder … it's just a difference!" Before you start sending me meltdown emails, ask yourself this: *why* is it such a problem to see autism as a disability? By law, disabilities have to be accommodated. Differences do not! Having a disability isn't necessarily good or bad. It just is. Being female isn't necessarily good or bad. It just is. Sure, there are complications, but the thing itself is not the problem. Do you know what *is* the problem? It's when we have to navigate those complications without the support of a life jacket—our accommodations—because we've advocated ourselves out of what little support already exists. Saying "it's just different" enough times might eventually catch up with us. Insurance companies and public resources are always looking for ways to cut funding. Within those screwed-up systems, differences aren't accommodated. Disabilities are!

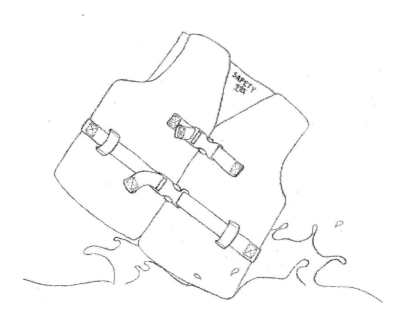

Chapter 3

What Autism Is

For some autistic people, "just a little difference" may represent their personal experience. But I think for most of us, that phrase leads to huge misconceptions about the reality of others' lives. Which leads me to some thoughts about what autism actually *is*.

Getting Technical: a developmental disorder

Autism is characterized by symptoms that usually appear in the first two years of life, which makes it a developmental disorder. For starters, let's get specific—and technical. The diagnosis of autism comes from the criteria laid out in the *Diagnostic and Statistical Manual of Mental Disorders* (American Psychiatric Association 2013), commonly referred to as DSM-5. Here's part of the section that applies to our discussion.

Diagnostic Criteria 299.00 (F84.0)

A. Persistent deficits in social communication and social interaction across multiple contexts, as manifested by the following, currently or by history (examples are illustrative, not exhaustive; see text):
1. Deficits in social-emotional reciprocity, ranging, for example, from abnormal social approach and failure of normal back-and-forth conversation; to reduced sharing of interests, emotions, or affect; to failure to initiate or respond to social interactions.
2. Deficits in nonverbal communicative behaviors used for social interaction, ranging, for example, from poorly integrated verbal and nonverbal communication; to abnormalities in eye contact and body language or deficits in understanding and use of gestures; to a total lack of facial expressions and nonverbal communication.
3. Deficits in developing, maintaining, and understanding

relationships, ranging, for example, from difficulties adjusting behavior to suit various social contexts; to difficulties in sharing imaginative play or in making friends; to absence of interest in peers....

B. Restricted, repetitive patterns of behavior, interests, or activities, as manifested by at least two of the following, currently or by history (examples are illustrative, not exhaustive; see text):
1. Stereotyped or repetitive motor movements, use of objects, or speech (e.g., simple motor stereotypies, lining up toys or flipping objects, echolalia, idiosyncratic phrases).
2. Insistence on sameness, inflexible adherence to routines, or ritualized patterns of verbal or nonverbal behavior (e.g., extreme distress at small changes, difficulties with transitions, rigid thinking patterns, greeting rituals, need to take same route or eat same food every day).
3. Highly restricted, fixated interests that are abnormal in intensity or focus (e.g., strong attachment to or preoccupation with unusual objects, excessively circumscribed or perseverative interests).
4. Hyper- or hyporeactivity to sensory input or unusual interest in sensory aspects of the environment (e.g., apparent indifference to pain/temperature, adverse response to specific sounds or textures, excessive smelling or touching of objects, visual fascination with lights or movement).

My purpose here is finding a bridge from the clinical understanding to the practical one. Over the years, many professionals and agencies adopted subcategories of autism but then later discarded them.

With the 2013 update, the DSM-5 introduced a three-tier system as a modifier to an autism diagnosis with the goal of identifying the level of support an autistic person requires based on their strengths and weaknesses. The language describing the levels is vague and subjective.

- Level One: "Requiring support"

- Level Two: "Requiring substantial support"

- Level Three: "Requiring very substantial support"

The DSM-5 attempts to clarify these terms by providing a few examples. Later, in Chapter 16, I'll provide some additional examples pulled from my interaction with hundreds of autistic people.

While some are still questioning if the distinctions offered by the three levels of support are actually helpful, they are *here,* and they are officially recognized by medical providers. If you're of the opinion that specifying the level of support required by a person's autism diagnosis is unhelpful, my advice to you would be to propose your alternative to the medical community. They constantly make updates. (Remember when Asperger's Syndrome was a thing?)

Getting Personal: where "my kind" fits on the spectrum

Technical and medical definitions aside, my hope here is to draw more attention to some factors most casual topic explorers are not seeing online. Autism is a really broad spectrum with many variances, many rates of progress, many differing needs. Decades ago, a common misconception was that all autism was a matter of being extremely affected, unable to communicate, often institutionalized … and onward the stereotypes would go. However, in our modern autism community, the most vulnerable now have the least representation. Where social media is concerned, you're *not* seeing equal representation of the autism spectrum. If you can speak your native language fluently, learn a variety of social rules, keep yourself safe without adult supervision, but occasionally punch yourself in the head when things go wrong, you might have the "just a little different" type of autism. But if you can't express yourself reliably, struggle to understand lots of language concepts, and occasionally bite the nearest person when you have a headache, you might have the "disorder" type of autism. Those of us perceived as "just a little different" are featured in movies, documentaries, and theatrical productions. But those of us perceived as "disordered" are featured only in medical journals, therapeutic conferences, and case studies. The correct term, the term we need to be talking about a lot more, is *profound autism,* which is defined as exhibiting minimal communication, having an IQ of less than 50, and requiring 24-hour supervision.

I know what you're thinking … "But that's just a small portion of the autism spectrum." Except according to a study recently cited by the Centers for Disease Control and Prevention (CDC), that's simply not true. Twenty-six percent of autistic people fit the criteria for profound autism (Hughes et al. 2023). By definition, most profoundly autistic people are *not* using social media in the traditional sense. Just because you don't see people like them as much as you do people like me, doesn't mean that they aren't real or aren't important. The spectrum concept means profound autism is as much a part of their reality, their personhood, as my kind is for me.

What kind of autism do I have? What kind of autism leads a person into a career doing therapy for other autistic people? I have the kind of autism that makes people say, "Everyone's a little autistic." I have the kind that makes others my age ask themselves, "I wonder if I have more than just ADHD?"

I have the kind of autism that seems to make people around me carefully examine their own idiosyncrasies. Often after hearing me talk, people scurry off on a web-based journey of self-discovery. I genuinely hope they find what they're looking for. But I suspect what they find may be pretty different from the kind of autism I have. My form of autism is different enough to be noticed, but not so noticeable as to make me seem out of place in an average social context. The takeaway can usually be summarized by saying I'm a little odd or quirky, but certainly not what some people think of as "special needs."

As a toddler, I had enough repetitive behaviors, meltdowns, and rigidity for my mom to notice, but I had too much language ability for pediatricians of that day to be willing to label me autistic. That misconception held until my pervasive academic and social failures grew severe enough that by age 10, my family called in a team of professionals. Said team emerged from several days of testing with a 46-page document labeling me as having learning disabilities—and autism!

What kind of autism did they find? They found the kind that makes me seem somewhat similar to you. I often say out loud what others are thinking. I have a systematic and methodical approach to just about everything, and I'm a firm believer in following rules that aren't stupid. Just like you, right? Maybe. Or maybe not. To those on that journey of self-discovery, allow me to offer a bit more insight.

I have the kind of autism that, during puberty, accidentally installed a metaphorical emergency-eject button in my brain. When stressors pile up, my autism has a quirky way of convincing me to slam my head into the nearest drywall to make the anxious thoughts stop, even if just for a moment. At work? Visiting doctors? On an airplane? In my room? Yes. The eject button stays present and functions just the same, regardless of the social setting or the number of people around me.

I have the kind of autism that keeps my closest relationships restricted to family and my roommates, even though most young adults start forging multiple intimate connections with people outside their household. I don't really "do" acquaintances or casual friends.

I have the kind of autism that tells me I'm *not* going to be okay if I fail to go to the grocery store every Sunday, carry my water bottle with me up to the mirror whenever I check my outfit, use only one color of plastic cup per week, turn on only the dresser lamp in the mornings, and sit in my closet after work.

When I "say the quiet parts out loud," and everyone laughs—maybe because they wish they had the guts to say what we all were thinking, or maybe because they're shocked by my audacity—a few people will sometimes remark, "The more time I spend around you, the more I wonder if I'm autistic." Funny thing … no one's ever said that to me after witnessing me lose my shit. Maybe because they're trying to be considerate? But *I* wonder if they just don't identify with those parts quite so much.

Now feels like the expected time to give the disclaimer that just because someone doesn't identify with the "my kind of autism" doesn't mean that they don't have autism. My intent in spelling out my personal perspective isn't to invalidate anyone's experiences or feelings. Rather, I want to illustrate how most people, including the ones who claim to relate to me so much, stop relating when they see the shit losing, the pervasive loneliness, and the rigidity which are equally a part of "my kind of autism." It's common for me to hear people profess how deeply their experience aligns with my own. Unfortunately, it's equally common for that conversation to grind to an awkward halt right at the most vulnerable point of my narrative. People can be really quick to say how much they understand and empathize—until it becomes incredibly obvious that they do neither.

The more I've repeated this style of interaction—and let me assure you, that's a lot—the more I've realized how much those experiences parallel what loved ones of those with profound autism face. Far more important than terminology is what those affected by profound autism encounter, not just from outsiders, but also from those inside the autism community. When newcomers to the world of autism get a glimpse of how tough reality is for the profoundly affected, they and their empathy usually fade quietly away. Unfortunately, some of the social media crowd who have "my kind of autism" don't just fade away. Instead, they have instigated an attack on the caregivers of the profound population for failing to embrace the autism mind as nothing other than delightfully different.

If you're just joining us, perhaps from a more peaceful place in the autism community—where brains can be thought of as "different" but never as "defective"—please understand something. I have a high-priority goal of bringing your attention to another kind of autism.

In 2021, the professional community was searching for a better way to describe the needs of folks with more extreme levels of disability. The *Lancet* Commission on the future of care and clinical research in autism proposed profound autism (Lord et al. 2021). While the purpose of this new term was to promote clarity of support needs, some are concerned it may actually be used to limit access to services.

I don't live in that place on the spectrum, but some of my clients do. The kind of autism I have brings pervasive loneliness, heightened emotional responses, and difficulty with executive functioning skills. The kind of autism *they* have brings hospital visits, social isolation, and difficulty with communicating basic wants and needs.

The differences between "my kind of autism" and "their kind of autism" deserve far more public awareness than it's getting. I believe one of society's biggest misconceptions about autism grows from the fact that certain autistic people are increasingly unseen, more or less drowned out by the far-greater communication abilities of others in different places on the spectrum. Accurately understanding autism means accurately seeing *the entirety of the spectrum.* To some readers, *they* are still *them.* An abstract concept. An entry in a book. To me, *they* have names. I see their faces. I watch their actions. I have a front-row seat to their struggles, joys, and disappointments—and those of their families as well.

In keeping with my fascination for finding practical, workable solutions, it's time to move into details about exactly how we remove barriers and cross these gaps between different realities.

Part 2: Communication

I get hundreds of comments from families who are desperate to hear their children's first words. So many times I hear a version of "I just want to know what's in his head." Although I'm not a parent, I have my own version of that angst in my work. One of the most urgent tasks we have is to provide an effective communication system for our clients. It is critical to every aspect of life. But communication with autistic people calls for a more detailed approach than just hoping this beloved child will magically absorb language.

To be effective, communication directed *to* autistic people usually needs to be much more direct and specific than most people are used to. That's an easy thing to say, and it can have many different meanings for almost every reader. So let's get … well … more *specific!*

Almost all humans sometimes struggle with making their language precise enough for accurate communication. We have so many possible meanings to the most basic of terms. What will happen if you ask someone, "Would you please bring me a chair?" Will they come back with a folding chair? A lawn chair? Or a recliner? The correct answer depends heavily on context, of course. But context is something that people with autism might not notice at all.

Social constructs often cause us to pad our requests or instructions, while autistic people often struggle to understand basic sentence structure—minus the verbal padding.

So again—specifically—how, exactly, do you make these things, this mystery of communication, happen? How do you encourage input? How do you reduce ambiguity? What are the options you have? Let's take a closer look.

Chapter 4

Making Social Demands Less Demanding

In our therapy, we will always start by focusing on what is important to the specific person we are serving. What language will be most meaningful to them? Simply labeling pictures to build vocabulary is not the way to start. Instead, we have to figure out what that particular person wants—and then give them a way to get that desire met. Does he love to get pulled down the hall in a wagon? Then he needs a word (spoken, on a device, or through signing) to let us know. Maybe "go" or "pull" or a directional gesture. Does she want to hear the theme song from *Dora the Explorer* on repeat, as loud as possible? Then we start with "song," "Dora," or whatever works to get that point across.

If you are in the situation of longing for *any* communication from your loved one, I hope that you are able to engage professionals who can help with that individualized process. Meanwhile, I do want to address one of the next most common comments I get from families whose children have gained language skills but aren't engaging in conversation: "They won't tell me anything about their day." "They never answer my questions."

Think about it this way. Whenever we ask questions, we are bestowing a burden to answer us. General conversational principles often rely on a question-answer-question-answer format. That pattern is frequently ineffective with autistic people, who may find it unmotivating or overwhelming. Or you might get responses that are less about engagement and more about avoidance. Worse yet, you might get a response similar to one of my clients: if I ask him "How was school?" he'll scream "Oh no, not again," then run and hide from me.

Candy Bowls: the power of declarative statements

If your conversation-opening questions are being ignored or shut down, I suggest you try using *declarative statements*. Declarative statements offer an opportunity to engage without the expectation or demand a question would carry. When trying to get people to understand declarative statements, I suggest thinking of it as setting out a bowl of candy. By comparison, think of asking questions as picking up the candy and attempting to feed it to someone.

Far too often, adults try to start a conversation with children by asking questions they believe the child is likely to want to answer.

- "Who's your favorite character in *Bluey*?"

- "What are you building with your Legos?"

- "How was your day at school?"

Rather than placing a social demand with the question (shoving candy in someone's face), you can offer up some statements of your own to see what happens (setting out the candy bowls).

- "My favorite character in *Bluey* is Bingo."

- "I am building a garage with my Legos."

- "My day was fun because I got to eat my favorite food."

Adapting questions to candy-bowl statements will take some practice and lots of patience. For starters, remember the principle that declarative statements are an optional invitation. They do not require a response! If the autistic person doesn't immediately respond with a corresponding statement, don't repeat or follow up with a question. Instead, try putting out a different bowl of candy. Present a statement on a different topic, or make another statement while engaged in an activity. This candy-presenting strategy also works as a replacement for questions you ask constantly in your daily interactions. Declarative statements focus on you, your thoughts, ideas, or opinions rather than the child's. Declarative statements are meant to be inviting. You use them to offer valuable interaction, so social demands feel more social and less demanding. Here are some more examples.

- **Not**: "Where is your Mario toy?"
  But: "Your cousin loves Mario, too. I wonder where your Mario toy is."

- **Not**: "What should we build?"
  But: "I know how to build a castle. I can make it really tall!"

- **Not**: "Do you want to go to the park or the pool today?"
  But: "I remembered there's no school today. We could go to the park. We could also go to the pool."

Of course, we cannot eternally tiptoe around the need to respond to direct questions or requests. I don't want to reduce the need for directness when specific information or actions have to happen.

However, especially with children, too many kids miss out on social engagement because of extreme avoidance of what they perceive as endless demands. You may not mean it that way, but plenty of autistic kids sure understand it that way.

Conversation Towers: building language with Legos

Depending on an individual's skill level and preferences, a visual reference might make it even easier to participate in conversation. So here's another option: a visual *conversation tower*. If the child you're talking to can read at least a little, you can try this to see if they like it. Find a set of building blocks, like Legos, that stack easily.

Here's how a conversation tower works. Write on the blocks the beginning of short, easy, open-ended phrases. Use identical pairs—the same words written on two blocks each, such as "I have," "I like," "I saw," "I'm going," or "I can."

Player One picks a block and makes a statement that finishes what's written on that block. They set the block down in front of the other player.

Player Two picks the second block with the same sentence, finishes the sentence their own way, and then stacks their block on top of Player One's block.

It might sound like this.

Player One says, "I had pizza for lunch."

Player Two says, "I had a sandwich for lunch."

Repeat with the next pair of blocks. You can switch who goes first and second. The game is finished when the players have used up all the blocks.

For learners who are ready for more challenging phrases, you can try longer, more complex phrases.

- "I was thinking about …."
- "When I went to …."
- "Something most people don't know is …."
- "I really don't like …."
- "At home I like to …."

Why does this help? Conversation blocks can provide structure to help *build* a statement, while still being open-ended enough for people to insert their own interests. Starting statements on the blocks need to be general so participants can fill in whatever is meaningful to them. When autistic people struggle with expressive language but show interest in conversation, this kind of strategy can make the type of interactions they seek more accessible. A conversation tower provides a physical cue for conversational turn-taking. The cues make practice possible in a way they might not otherwise be able to discern.

Chapter 5

Reducing Ambiguity

Specificity: choosing words carefully

Questions that are too ambiguous can cause anxiety. When people on the spectrum feel anxious, they usually have more difficulty responding. Being autistic and trying to navigate broad questions is kind of like playing *Tetris* with your eyes closed. As ridiculous as that might sound, let me explain. Non-autistic people get to play eyes-open *Tetris*. They can see and use the blocks already in place to decide about incoming blocks. The blocks already visible to them are contextual information that allows

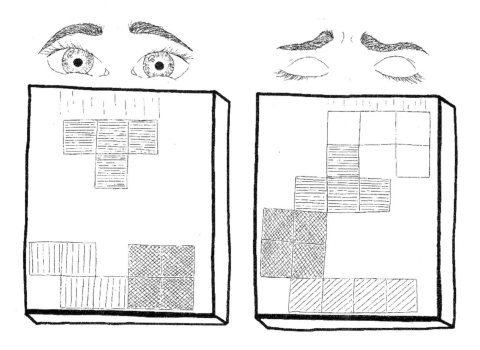

them to generate a suitable response when someone asks an open-ended question. Those blocks they can see at the bottom of the screen might include what information another person already knows, what they're interested in hearing about, and how that fits into a specific relationship dynamic. Autistic people can't always see those existing blocks. So we often feel like we play the game with our eyes closed. We struggle to see or interpret the context surrounding broad questions.

As an autistic person, it's hard for me to know how your question fits in with what you *already know* compared to what you *want to know*. You can fix that by phrasing your question to tell me explicitly what you're trying to find out.

> **Rather than:** "What have you been up to lately?"
>
> **Try:** "Do you have any cool projects coming up?"
> **Or:** "Have you done anything fun lately with your dog?"

Being more specific will let me know where your question fits. That way, I won't have to make a blind guess.

The area of ambiguous questioning became a huge issue for me after *Love On the Spectrum* aired. Several interview requests arrived every month. Almost every time, I was asked, "What was it like to be on the show?" My mind would immediately flood with a thousand ways to answer! What was it like to deal with the filming equipment? To go on a date? To interact with the public?

I always wanted to answer correctly, even if "correct" was just a matter of opinion. I was hypersensitive to any modifiers the interviewers might include. For example, if the interviewer asked, "What was it like preparing to be filmed?" my answer would expound on all the different preparations that were immensely stressful. We had to clean the house extensively, take measures for COVID, buy new date outfits, and coordinate appointments to suit the schedules of multiple people.

But if that same interviewer had asked, "What was it like to be filmed?" … well, that's entirely different. I would say that the filming was a bit intimidating at first, but the intimidation quickly faded because of how kind the film crew was.

Yet for me, focusing on those specific modifiers could paralyze me because I didn't want to answer the wrong question. I'm fortunate to have the language skills to say, "Can you be more specific?" but many others on the spectrum do not have that ability. People sometimes interpret that gap as autistic people being uninterested in conversation. However, this ambiguity thing is what so often stalls us out!

Try taking a moment to think about your question before you ask. *How*, exactly, can we reduce that ambiguity?

- **Someone**: "What's wrong?"
  Me (thinking): I don't know what you mean. What's wrong with me? Or you? Or at school? At home? With my family? Or with the idiot who started this mess?

- **Someone**: "Tell me about yourself. What are some things you enjoy?"
  Me (thinking): Well, I enjoy a lot of things from lots of different categories ….

- **Someone**: "What is something you wish people knew about you?"
  Me (thinking): Which people? And what do they already know? I can't possibly select an answer that would fit that big of a question without more information.

In any given situation, try to train yourself to ask for exact, specific information rather than anything even remotely general. Try to use questions more like these.

- "What book are you reading in English class this week?"

- "What outside activities did you do this weekend with your family?"

- "What video games are you playing in the evenings with your online friends?"

This concept goes way beyond conversational questions. It applies to helping solve problems, giving directions, and clarifying misunderstandings. As someone on the spectrum, I recognize you may not completely follow an idea I'm trying to communicate, but it's helpful to me to know exactly *which* part you need me to clarify. Use simple but *specific* questions to isolate what you're asking me to say or do. This precision tells me what I need to change or elaborate on so you can understand.

- "Which part of this problem makes you upset?"

- "What needs to change in the room right now?"

- "What can I do to make this easier?"

- "Tell me more about how your idea would help clarify the confusion."

- "Which part of this task do you need my help with?"

- "When you said *(idea)*, I was thinking *(thought)*. Tell me how it's different."

For these suggestions to help you in communicating with autistic people, you'll really need to keep individualism in mind. Not everyone on the spectrum struggles with open-ended communication any more than they do with overly broad questions. And everyone who does have those challenges will have them to a different degree. But if you are coming from a place of wanting to increase effective communication with an autistic individual, my advice is to aim for specificity and learn the correct balance point for the particular person with whom you're trying to communicate. I acknowledge that anyone, anywhere, can find ambiguity difficult to work through. But for many autistic people, it can completely halt the progress of a communicative exchange.

It's also fair to acknowledge that not everyone will be deeply concerned with getting it right. Not because they don't care, but because they may not understand the importance of certain questions or situations. And some of our more language-challenged friends may eagerly respond—but with an answer that is factually incorrect or completely out of context.

Sequence: orienting to person, place, and time

I've found that using a visual tool can help me fill in gaps when I am trying to understand my clients' responses. Imagine you hear something like this: "Today the teacher said I was gonna be in trouble on the bus and Ben called me annoying!"

That's a story with a middle, but no beginning or end. We need better info, and we need some sequence. If you want to help, work in the moment. Ask them to pause for a moment. "Hold on! Let's make sure I understand all the parts." Grab a paper and divide it into sections—at least three. Write down the part you understand in the middle section: *Ben said you were annoying!* Perhaps add *trouble* in the section after that to represent the bus driver's part. Show them the chart.

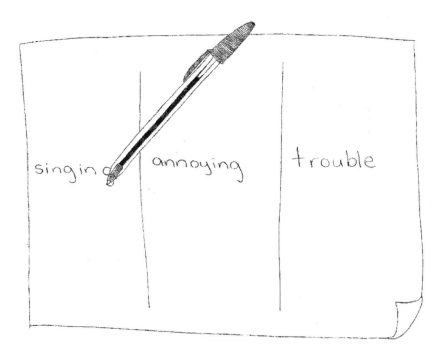

Your questions now will be similar to what's described above. Point to

Ben's words; then point to the empty first section: "What was happening right before Ben said you were annoying?" Maybe you'll hear something like "I was singing! Because I love to sing and I'm really good at it!" Now we have more clues.

"You were singing. Ben called you annoying. What happened next?" You might hear more. "I told him that was really rude and it hurts my feelings! I told him if he kept saying that, I was going to punch him!"

Depending on what additional information might be unearthed with your chart and more attention to sequence, you now have more to work with. It's important to summarize your sequence. Give the autistic person a chance to clarify that, yes, that's what happened, or no, I need to add more information. For some, this visual reference may need to contain pictures rather than words.

When I have a clear idea of the sequence of what happened, I can shape my suggestions on how to either manage the remaining effects of the situation or how to prevent situations like that from occurring in the future. While this tool won't work for everyone, it does, at least, help illustrate your attempt at understanding.

Stress the Action: incorporating verbs

One suggestion that always stays at the very top of my list for reducing ambiguity is pretty simple. Use verbs! You might be interacting with a fully language-abled adult. Or you might be engaging with a child just learning conversational skills. It's possible you might be communicating with completely non-vocal people who use writing or a tablet to tell you what they want. In all those cases, a primary rule for effective interaction with autistic people is to use *verbs* to let the person know what to do.

Yes, I understand some people view being direct as being rude. But in these situations, you're interacting with people who struggle with comprehending language, understanding social customs, and interpreting ambiguity. For us, I assure you it's not rude. If your listener is still working to comprehend basics, easing into suggestions with lots of extra word padding and social niceties will not get you where you need to go. It might make *you* feel more comfortable, as though you're being more polite. But I promise ... it's not helping us! Here's an example that might illustrate the problem.

Let's suppose Melissa needs to exit a room through a particular door. Jay is standing in her way. She says "Excuse me!" But Jay doesn't move. She tries again, using more words: "Watch out! I need to come through." But Jay still doesn't move.

But genuine success happens when, after two unsuccessful attempts, Melissa finally considers what she needs Jay (not herself) to do, right now, with the information she's giving him. Melissa thinks this through, then says, "Jay, please take a few steps back." Jay now understands exactly what he is supposed to do with her communication. He steps back and allows Melissa to pass through the door.

Direct communication tells someone exactly what they should *do*. No matter what piece of information you give, the autistic person needs to be able to eliminate guesswork. Hidden intentions or subjective implications can be very difficult for an autistic person to pick up on. Direct communication using verbs can sound like these sentences.

- "Walk with me."

- "Put it down."

- "First, listen to him talk. Then he will listen to you."

- "Tell me about the problem."

- "Look at the menu; then pick one."

Specific verbs help you communicate as directly as possible. Verbs help you get to the heart of what you're trying to convey. Ambiguity lessens. Clarity increases.

Straightforward: building trust

Direct communication builds trust with autistic people. I know this from personal experience. My most trustworthy relationships don't require me to pick up on all those implied meanings, indirect requests, or the not-so-mutual understanding of social customs. Conversely, I distrust people who make requests through sideways hints. Especially when I need explicit instruction about something, I get uncomfortable when people won't directly explain.

For instance, if I ask my medical providers for more information, I often receive a general response such as "This is to make sure you're healthy." I get the impression they find providing explicit information to be bothersome. However, without the information, I may be reluctant to follow through with the medical advice. That combination of problems—medical providers, indirect answers, and way too many assumptions—finally led me to attend doctor appointments armed with written instructions from me. I insist all medical providers review and agree to my instructions before they touch me or begin any kind of evaluation. The wording in my letter? "*I have a diagnosis of autism. At times it is difficult during stressful situations to communicate my wishes. The purpose of this letter is to communicate my wishes prior to this appointment to avoid any miscommunication. The goal of today's appointment is [explanation]. I am choosing to decline any intervention which involves needles due to sensory aversions. I have read and understand the risks of declining. Please explain all procedures first to help me better cooperate with treatment. I am open to listening to any information you would like to provide on this topic; however, I ask that you honor when consent is withdrawn.*"

That's the kind of direct wording autistic people will thrive on. Ambiguous or incomplete communication leaves us unsure about how to respond. When communication is direct, leaving no room for guesswork, autistic people have the best chance to understand.

Chapter 6

Improving the Odds

Who remembers the Fisher Price Little People? All those cool, tiny little dudes with different hats, different clothes, different faces! They didn't have feet, but they had round bottoms that fit into everything from their tractor seats to their household furniture. When I was very young, I carried these folks with me most places, carefully tucked into a clear plastic holder. My mom, never one to miss an opportunity, often used them in role-playing to teach me how to talk to other people. Whether as part of a planned trip to visit relatives or a short-notice trip to the grocery store, one would be designated as me. Others would be the people we'd

likely encounter. We practiced greetings. We practiced possible questions. We practiced options for answers. I was extremely verbal, and Mom often had to do as much work to get me to shut up as she did to get me to talk appropriately!

I realize I had skills and advantages in my childhood many autistic people do not have. Not everyone is verbal at a young age; not everyone has a mom with the time and energy to engage in role play. But I do want to emphasize that practice is a tremendously valuable tool for the autistic community. I know that "practice makes perfect" applies to the world at large. In my world it is more often true that "practice makes possible." Whether you are someone on the spectrum yourself or someone supporting an autistic person, I challenge you to spend some time in practice.

Here are a few more strategies that I encourage you to try.

Stop. Wait: let's lose the double questions

I have noticed that people frequently ask multiple questions in a row, often adding new questions to add context to the first one. Many of us on the spectrum find this overwhelming, leaving us confused about how to even start an answer.

I suggest you think about what your actual question is, ask it as directly as possible, and then wait for an answer. That stop-and-wait approach seems challenging to lots of neurotypical people. They rush to fill in the silence, which I presume feels awkward to them. But that pause gives us time to process and put forth an answer.

> **Bad example:** "When did your dad call? What did he say about going on the trip? Do you need my help to get ready to go?"

> **Good example:** "When did your dad call?" Stop and wait for an answer. "What did he say about going on the trip?" Stop and wait for an answer. "Do you need my help to get ready to go?" Stop and wait for an answer.

If someone gives an incomplete answer or appears to leave out information, a simple, "Tell me more about that" can be effective in instructing people to expand. You can also go back to the visual aid we discussed earlier to help fill in gaps.

Conversational Rabbit Trails: getting back on track

Just be aware that practice can never rule out the unexpected! A friend of mine, Michael, had a chance to get some of his cool artwork incorporated into a company's cloth designs. So his parents, teachers, and therapists engaged in structured practice to prepare him for what a future job interview might look like. They carefully went through how to shake hands, where to find the appropriate seat, and what information to provide. When it came time to sit down with the fabulous business owner, all the preparation paid off as Michael maneuvered through the interview as planned. To finish up, the business owner offered up a final opportunity: "Michael, do you have any questions for me?"

Michael's eyes lit up and a big smile broke out. He absolutely glowed. "Yes! I do!" he said. "Have you watched *Barney & Friends*: 'May I Help You?' on a JVC VHS tape on April 11, 2020?" And he was off down the rabbit trail of his passion for all things Barney. Not at all pertinent to the issue at hand, but far more interesting to him!

Many readers will have encountered this. When an autistic person doesn't understand a question itself or the importance of a question, they might simply divert paths by giving a detailed response on a related topic. If you find yourself listening to a lengthy, parallel explanation or something totally unrelated, you'll need to back up and narrow down your question. The person you asked might not have understood what you wanted to know.

Depending on the individual, it's also possible that they understood but chose a detour. The question might be unappealing, and they avoided answering by choosing a more favored topic. As a kid, I was often definitely guilty as charged in this department. My go-to topic for avoiding less interesting, unwanted subjects was *The Lion King*. Mom says

I would start reciting a scene for her at any given moment. The longer the better. It would take considerable redirecting to get me back on track. The origin of the behavior might be as simple as Michael's, when he was thinking, "Oh wow, finally! Here is someone who wants to know about all my favorite topics!" Just like he did, when I was given an opportunity to interpret a question as, "Tell me all about it," I jumped at any chance to share all possible information!

In a general social conversation, you might tolerate an off-topic diatribe. But if you still need to know whatever it was you started out with, then you'll need to redirect your autistic conversational partner back to the pertinent question. To the extent possible, I recommend letting them finish before reopening the needed discussion with more specific direction. If time doesn't allow that option, you may need to set a schedule in the near future when you can listen to their information.

For instance, consider one of my clients, a teen boy who needs to learn about hygiene. When I ask about grooming practices, his preferred response is to list off the birth years of the entire Star Wars cast. My response needs to be respectful of his passion for Star Wars while directing him back to the topic at hand: "It sounds like you're really excited about that information. I'll make sure to save time for you to tell me more after we work on hair brushing."

Plain Language: best practices for writing

Writing also needs to be direct. Whether for official documentation or for general communication, the best practice I can recommend is called

plain language. That's not a term I made up; it's now quite widely recognized and accepted as best practice for many types of writing. Plain language is writing designed to ensure a reader can understand the message as quickly, simply, and completely as possible. In many countries, laws mandate public agencies use plain language to increase the accessibility of programs and services.

Plain language is neither unprofessional nor talking down to the reader. It is simply a way of writing that is to the point with the goal of helping improve communication and taking less time to read and understand. When writing to people on the autism spectrum, plain language is the written embodiment of most of what we've already discussed—direct and specific. Why is it helpful? Better question: why is it *necessary*? Let me give you my personal point of view, which might be more complex than most, but the idea still carries! Being severely dyslexic means I cannot read all the unnecessary social fluff in your email. Being "mildly autistic" means I also don't care about the social fluff in your email. Beyond a greeting, well wishing, and reason for initiating contact, I tap out. Whether it's autism, dyslexia, just a product of my age, or even my social media experience, I am particularly intolerant to rambling text that provides excessive details.

If those weren't enough reasons to hate "wordy," I struggle with *working memory*. This is slightly different from short-term memory in that working memory isn't really meant to stick around or have a lasting impact. When you complete any multi-step task, working memory is responsible for keeping track of where you are in the task, what still needs to be done, and making any adjustments that need to be accounted for in the moment. Deficits in working memory make it hard to sift through extra information and remember what's required of me. I can either read (stumble through) long bodies of text over and over until I eventually grasp the subject, or I can quickly absorb shorter, more concise text and know what to do with it. But both to read it and remember it long enough to understand the entire process can be challenging since I've been told before that I have the memory of a goldfish!

If you want to give yourself an assignment of improving your writing and using more plain language, I suggest using the powerful tool of the internet. Search for "plain language list of principles," and watch how many sites appear. Almost all of them will include some paraphrase of the following characteristics:

- organized to serve reader needs,

- omits excess words,

- uses "you" pronouns and present tense,

- consists of short sections with short paragraphs,

- uses base and active verbs instead of hidden or passive verbs,

- employs lists and tables to illustrate complex concepts, and

- uses *must* to express requirements (rather than the ambiguous *shall*).

If you want to get really serious about studying the idea, you might want to start with the official government checklist on the topic, where you'll find all the above and more.

plainlanguage.gov/resources/checklists/checklist/

Take a Moment: option of written responses

Whether you're a parent, friend, or therapist, don't overlook the potent tool of giving the option of communicating in writing rather than speech for those who are fluent in that skill. Basic communication? Social interaction? Problem solving? Conflict resolution? Yes! All of the above.

For those with the ability to write, the extra time to consider words might just lead you to a place you'd never get to in spoken words. I tend to express my emotions in a less combative way when I have a backspace option, and that's going to be true for other autistic people, whether adult or child.

You can make use of this option—or not—depending on the autistic person's preference *and* ability. For those who have adequate cognitive and communication abilities, I suggest asking: "I have some questions for you. Would it be easier for you to tell me the answers or to write them?"

Part 3: Behaviors

"You don't have to use yelling, running, or falling to the floor to show me what you need." This was me recently talking to a nine-year-old client.

She looked up at me from her current position sprawled on the ground in a heap and said, "What do you mean?"

An enormous challenge for me when trying to get the rest of the world to interact more successfully with autistic people is enabling them to answer that little girl's question in scores of other scenarios!

When autistic people have a hard time communicating their needs to those around them, they might rely on behaviors that are *un*helpful! Think of it this way: if you had socks but didn't have any shoes, and you were expected to run an errand, well … you'd probably put on what you *have* and head off to do the errand. Walking around Walmart in sock feet might confuse some people. But from your point of view, you were just using what you have, because there wasn't a better option available.

Autistic people may have a variety of maladaptive behaviors, some more common than others, that they are using because it's what they have, although far more effective means can be made available. In the case of my nine-year-old client, falling to the floor was definitely not the most effective way to communicate a specific desire. But for her, like with so many autistic people, that behavior might be the only thing she has—it's her socks when she actually needs shoes.

Revisiting that conversation above, I explained to her in specific terms, "If you tell me 'I need more time to play!' I would understand right away that you weren't ready to leave." While this is a simplistic example with a

young child, the point remains that teaching a contextually helpful skill—
a different behavior—is like giving someone shoes when they had only
socks. In a broader context of general interaction between autistic people
and neurotypical people, it's a good framework to keep in mind as we
consider the different behaviors that are common to autism.

Chapter 7

Meltdowns

Recently, while in Chicago to speak to a group about autism, I added a few days to the trip for sightseeing. I have a pretty robust skill set for coping with frustrations, but let me tell you ... on this trip I used every ounce of the repertoire to rent a car, navigate the city, plan meals and activities, deal with traffic, handle getting away from unexpected situations (lots of civil protests in the city while I was there), and manage my time effectively. The trip was fun, but arguably one of the more difficult adult experiences I've yet had.

On the way back to the airport we got lost a few times. I didn't have enough time for lunch and was unable to get a souvenir I'd wanted badly. In terms of stress tolerance, I'd exhausted my supply. By the time I boarded the plane and realized I wasn't going to get the window seat I'd booked, my tolerance level was at zero. Yeah ... that "robust skill repertoire" includes being able to ask others for help, but I do need at least some tolerance left in order to *access* said repertoire! Profanities came flying out of my mouth, and my fist went flying into my face.

Rather than lecturing me on proper airplane etiquette, my travel companion first positioned herself to shield me from view and gave me some warm words of empathy, expressing her understanding of the hard time I was having. She then solved the window seat problem by politely asking to switch seats with a kind stranger.

Meltdowns are a nearly universal part of the autistic experience across the spectrum. Let's explore why they happen and what can be done.

What Is Happening: overtaken by overwhelm

You've probably heard the screams. You may have seen the flying objects. You may have seen humans, perhaps large as well as small, on the ground kicking and screaming. Perhaps you've seen it in the last day—or hour. Meltdowns are frequently a fact of autistic life, so the operative questions become about averting, coping, and stabilizing. The most critical factor I need to get you to understand? Someone having a meltdown is not *giving* you a hard time. They are *having* a hard time.

Autism meltdowns are highly emotional and/or uncontrollable behavioral responses to an overwhelming situation or event. Though triggers can look different for each person, meltdowns happen because situational demands or expectations exceed a person's current level of ability. That level of ability is subject to change. It varies not only from person to person, but from day to day and from one circumstance to the next.

Here are some common factors that can contribute to someone's ability—or *in*ability—to handle stress:

- changes in routine (see Chapter 8),

- disrupted expectations (see Chapter 8),

- inability to communicate a need or desire (see Chapter 5),

- failure to understand someone else's communication (see Part 2),

- not getting enough sleep,

- not eating on time, or

- uncomfortable sensory input (see Chapter 10).

Let me be clear. Bad parenting or a lack of personal discipline do not cause autism meltdowns. These behaviors result from an unmet need and/or a missing skill, leaving the autistic person overwhelmed with emotion and having no adequate skills or tools with which to cope.

Meltdowns might be most noticeable in children, since they've had far less chance to learn coping strategies or redirects, but never fool yourself that it's not sometimes happening to the autistic adult in your world. Not visible—or not visible *yet*—doesn't mean the probability isn't there. Someone can present with all requisite skills and poise, yet still have times of experiencing severe issues. Beyond that, keep in mind that in the world of autistic adults most of us have less access to support from others than children do, and perhaps no chances at all for "do-overs." If you fail to control a meltdown adequately, maybe you won't have a job anymore.

I have enough language skill that I can usually advocate for myself. However, add in a long day at work coupled with a few changes in my nightly routine, and *bam*. Suddenly a small conflict with my roommate can turn into a disproportionate emotional explosion. Without the added stressors, I could normally hear out the conflict scenario and help with problem solving. Unfortunately for me, the daily stressors of life can suck me in and rob me of that ability.

At that point, my autism inhibits my ability to recognize internal cues that should tell me to step back and make a change so a meltdown won't occur.

So let's talk about how to help when the inevitable meltdown happens.

What Not to Do: no teaching allowed

First, let's clarify what doesn't help. Feeling intense emotions can make even the most basic communication far more difficult, if not impossible. Meltdowns are challenging for everyone involved! Sometimes meltdowns can include behavior that is disruptive or dangerous. You might see crying, screaming, dropping to the floor, physical aggression, property destruction, or even self injury. A meltdown will look different for each person, and every person may experience different intensity each time, depending on the circumstances. It's easier said than done, but it's critically important that the person providing support during the meltdown stay calm. De-escalation must happen first.

When I'm extremely upset, I feel like a sinking boat taking on water. All of my resources, or coping skills, are on top of the water. They're my oxygen. As my boat begins to sink, it compromises my ability to access the oxygen, making me act frantically to maintain control. If the boat takes on too much water, I become so upset that I can no longer reach my coping skills. I can't reach the oxygen. I have to wait until I can calm down or swim back up to the top before I can communicate properly or problem-solve constructively.

With that frame of reference, it's absolutely critical to remember this: a meltdown is *not* a teaching moment! Discussions of triggers and contributing factors may be useful in making adjustments *before* a meltdown happens. But *before* is the pivotal word, because whether assessing for your child or trying to regulate yourself, once the meltdown arrives, there is no more learning opportunity. People can't absorb new information when they're in the middle of an emotional crisis. It's not possible. We simply *cannot* successfully teach someone emotional regulation or problem-solving skills when they're that upset. They won't hear you, and even if they did, they're extremely unlikely to retain what's said. Instruction can occur *only* when they are relatively calm so that their brains can retain the information.

Think about the last baseball game you watched. When someone hits a ball out of bounds … it's a foul ball, period. Players don't waste effort trying to coax the ball a little closer to where it should have gone. Instead, they throw it back and do the whole thing over again. Supporting autistic people during meltdowns should work the same way. Teaching can move forward only when a person's emotions are back "in play"—like the baseball. Just like the batter needs to wait for the foul ball to be thrown back, those providing support need to wait for the tense moments to pass before attempting to teach emotional regulation or problem-solving strategies.

What to Do: how to get the ball back in play

All that said, I'm not suggesting people in a support role just stand around and wait. Go get the ball and throw it back! The baseball game represents effective teaching. The baseball's position represents the person's emotional state. Three tips to throw that ball back into play?

- Make sure everyone is safe.

- Let them know you are empathetic.

- Help them regain a sense of control.

Let's look at each of those three tips a little more closely.

First, remember that autistic people may resort to extremely disruptive behavior to communicate what their words cannot, which is: "I'm in distress!" So before you do anything else, make sure that both the individual and the surrounding people are safe. This step may involve removing items or people from the environment, providing some cloak of dignity through a makeshift barrier from the rest of the world, and/or adding some element of comfort and safety such as a pillow or blanket.

Second, even if you don't know whether the person understands your words, express empathy through your tone, facial expression, and body positioning. For me, realizing someone understands what's happening can feel like a lifeline in a stormy sea. Just acknowledging someone's overwhelmed state of mind can make them feel heard. I'll be the first to admit my own emotional and behavioral responses during a meltdown can be "over the top." But it's possible to validate and understand someone's feelings without justifying their response. You can put the ball back in play by offering understanding and compassion through empathy statements.

- "That seems really upsetting."
- "I'm sorry that bothers you so much."
- "It's really hard when your toy is missing."

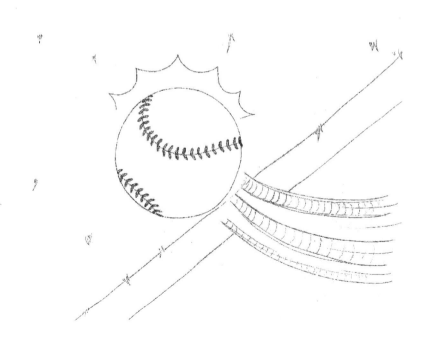

Third, amid a meltdown, we feel completely out of control. Try restoring at least a little sense of autonomy by giving choices. How you approach that differs somewhat depending on the person's age, skill level, and verbal ability. It might be as simple as switching to a window seat—or not!

Remember that the initial choices may need to be extremely small and concrete.

- "Do you want to sit here or there?"

- "Do you want the lights off or on?"

- "Do you want me to hug you or to give you space?"

With the tiniest bit of autonomy re-established, you can hopefully work up to bigger options such as:

- reading a book,

- going for a walk, or

- drawing a picture.

Depending on circumstances, another strategy might be to explain how you can help. So, for example, if a child is frustrated in a social situation, you might say, "I'm good at helping kids make sure they're heard by their friends. If you want, I can help you come up with something to say to them."

Allow the child to hear *how* you plan to help and to give input. Also, know that having some time and space to themselves for a little while can be helpful. They might be at a point where any additional verbal or sensory input will make things worse, not better.

This same general strategy can be adjusted for age and autonomy. Even with language-abled adults like myself, you can use direct language to offer help. This could sound like, "I can tell you're upset about the change in schedule," then transition to "How can I help you get started on what happens next?" If nothing else, something as simple as "What can I do right now to make you feel better?" could get a calmer conversation started. But you need to listen and heed the answer, even if the response is for you to go away for a little while and give the person some time to process and relax.

Patience! An intensely upset person may not make an immediate choice. That's not necessarily rudeness or stubbornness. They might still be grasping for their oxygen and barely able even to hear you, let alone respond rationally. In that case, *wait* and "ride out the storm" a little longer. Then re-issue your offer. But don't get caught in a power struggle that *requires* them eventually to make a choice. Sometimes you may have to guess at what that choice might be, move forward, and adjust if it doesn't work.

Of course depending on who's reading this book for what reason, "you" could be … well … *you*! Having this same conversation with yourself and therefore making advance plans, can help you learn to moderate your own pre-meltdown behaviors. Enlist a trusted person's help if that would make you feel more calm when you're overwhelmed. Tell that person ahead of time what might help or what they should offer, even if it's something as simple as "Help me find a place where I can be completely alone for about 10 minutes."

What Happens Before: the impact of setting events

People often point to a single factor as the cause of a meltdown. But from an insider's perspective, the lead-up often plays a larger role than one single event. For instance, I know how to respond when my schedule changes, when the environment is loud, or if I experience conflict with another person. But when multiple triggers occur close together, the combination wears on my ability to cope.

A parallel problem can be found not in multiple events, but in one relatively minor trigger that follows you around for an extended period. It doesn't have to be huge. It's just something you dislike or find annoying, but you can't get rid of it. In my work, these factors are called *setting events*. It's a little more subtle than one big abrupt event or even a whole series of smaller ones that can be easily observed. A setting event is something that occurs within the context of your day, stays with you for the whole day, colors your entire day, and will not leave. It's probably not observable to others. It's as though you had to smell a rotten, repulsive odor from the time you woke up to the time you went home, and you had no means to eliminate the stench. You, the autistic person with the limited communication skills, have to carry it and cope with it for an entire day. You don't understand the social cues for how it might be acceptable to ask for help.

Maybe your setting event started as having tried something new for breakfast, but you hated it. So you didn't finish. Then you ran off to work or school still hungry. But you were in such a rush that you forgot your lunch. Now it's hours later, after your normal lunch time, and you're starving. Everyone else has eaten, and nobody realizes how hungry you are. Nobody can hear your stomach rumbling. Nobody can tell it's giving you a headache. Why not say so? Why not go get something to eat? Maybe you're not free to leave, and you don't understand if it's okay to ask permission. Maybe you're also trying to decipher a complicated discussion going on around you, possibly among several people, and you don't know whether someone might get angry if you ask your teacher or co-worker to do a fast-food drive through. Maybe you don't get this problem solved for the whole day. Now you arrive home and discover the milk carton in your fridge is empty. You've been starving all day, but, without milk, you can't make mac and cheese. That's the final straw, and the resulting meltdown looks all out of proportion to your roommates.

Your trigger might be something very specific, like your hunger, that you don't understand how to fix. Or your trigger might be much more vague than hunger, like an undefined smell of rotting food when you can't even figure out where the smell is coming from. Either way, the problem has been grating on your nerves all day, and the empty milk carton was the final straw, triggering a heavy, uncontrollable emotional response—a meltdown. For autistic individuals, a setting event can have a profound effect on our ability to handle challenging situations, even if those setting events seem uneventful to everyone else. As human beings, we each have different amounts of tolerance for certain issues. For example, some of us can perform really well under pressure. Having an important deadline or being observed by a group can motivate us to concentrate or work harder. Others are unable to perform when the pressure gets high. They cave under stress and don't perform well.

Every autistic person and also everyone around them can benefit from understanding which events will set the stage for a meltdown. If possible, talk about them. Acknowledge them and try to plan ahead. The more awareness you have, the more likely you can work in advance to regulate and control situations, possibly avoiding meltdowns.

Advance preparation is a much more difficult process for the profoundly affected who can't tell you as directly what they need. Consider some form of written record-keeping of meltdowns to look for common triggers, patterns of days and times, repeated issues in certain places, etc. The more detailed your understanding, the better you can anticipate and hopefully avoid meltdowns. I've had many a chat with frustrated parents who can't tell me—because they can't remember—exactly what sequence led up to a hard episode. Life is stressful and complex. We think we won't forget, but time gets in the way of that for all of us. Knowledge is power! Some kind of journal or record—whatever works best for you—detailing the circumstances can give you a valuable reference tool.

Chapter 8

Change: the Common Enemy

Recently I was working in my office (ironically, writing a piece on cognitive rigidity), when a coworker interrupted to ask, "If you aren't doing therapy sessions this week, why are you here? Can't you work on that project from home?"

I paused for a second and just said, "No, I can't work from home."

Except that's not really true!

I have all the things one would need for working at home. I have the space, the equipment, and the internet. Yet I don't work from home. You know why? I don't work from home because I've never worked from home. It's not possible because I've never done it. Working in the office is my routine. So instead, I commute 40 minutes, one way, to sit at my office desk rather than the desk that's 10 steps away from my bed. Autism might cause me some inconvenience at times, but at least it doesn't prevent me from appreciating the irony of situations like this.

Whether ironic, mildly entertaining, or just plain frustrating, disrupted plans often rule as the great enemy of stable days and moods for autistic people … and their families. Why is change such a problem? Almost all humans, autistic or not, do better with structured routine than random activity, but autistic people have a tendency to be more dependent on routines than others.

It's a Big Deal: an autistic perspective on routines

Here's my perspective on why we resist change. Our routines help us feel safe. When you live in a world where it's hard to read people, to understand and predict their behavior, any amount of change can make life feel more chaotic than it already is. Routines give us a sense of stability, as well as some portion of our universe that we understand. For many of us, our routines can feel like the only factors we control. Consequently, disruptions to those routines are extremely challenging.

Since childhood I've always had a hard time with change, especially as it relates to my schedule. From the time I wake until I go to bed, my brain likes to run through all my scheduled events over and over. This mindset is extremely common among autistic people. Even if they don't rehearse everything the way I do, many, or perhaps even most, will subconsciously expect the exact details, step by step, all day.

Completing a familiar routine can comfort us in the same way that snuggling up with a warm blanket, drinking tea, and sitting by the fire can comfort someone who enjoys those things. Alteration, especially abrupt

alteration, can feel like discovering cat pee on your blanket, having only damp, smoking wood for the fireplace, and half-choking on tea you accidentally inhaled rather than swallowed. You expected warm feelings and cozy vibes, only to be cold, disgusted, and gasping for air. Sure, gasping for air might happen in the least life-threatening way, but it's no more comfortable at the moment.

Even if it's not a regular routine, unmet expectations can create that same out-of-control feeling. Recently, I took a much-anticipated drive with a friend to a lake where we'd planned an afternoon of fun and sun with the dogs frolicking in the water. I'd thought about this outing for days. We filled the drive to the lake with excited anticipation ... until we arrived and found ourselves staring at a weedy bog with a small, scummy puddle far beyond what used to be the beach. Forget letting the dogs swim. We'd have exposed ourselves to 13 different diseases just by dipping one toe into the mess. "Lake? What lake?? Where did it go? I mean, what did they do??" I shrieked my frustration to the world. "Roll it up and move it??" It stayed pretty noisy inside that car for a while. Fortunately, my friend was fine with my high state of emotion. She even helped me by indulging in some exaggerated role play about our frustration, giving me an outlet to kick and scream metaphorically, decompress, and be able to move on with my day. Okay, would anyone have been disappointed? Sure. But as with so many other factors in autism, our brains respond in ways quite out of sync with practical reality. My level of intense frustration about disrupted plans can be a little over the top compared to what's typical in regular society, and knowing that's true doesn't always help me turn it off.

I think it's important to understand the devastating feelings change can bring to us who are on the spectrum. Here's what happens for me. My brain is constantly running through all the activities coming up in my day—in great detail and with constant regularity. I don't consciously engage in repetitive rehearsing of upcoming events. My brain just does this in the background all the time! I am almost perpetually imagining myself going through my next activities.

I am picturing my entire day's activities in my mind:

- the roads I'll take on my way to work,

- the room I'll set my things in when I get there,

- all the rooms I'll be in throughout the day,

- what other people will be in there with me,

- the specific place I'll sit at lunch,

- the specific sweatpants I'll change into when I go home, and

- where I'll lie on the floor while I scroll through social media.

To me, change in my routine destroys my mental images, shattering those carefully constructed pictures into millions of pieces. I must now shift from the automatic pilot replay of expectations to the conscious work of creating a replacement image. That effort can feel insurmountable.

I often run into this problem when making weekend plans. Maybe I've planned where I want to go, who will come with me, and what we'll do, but I've forgotten to loop these other people into the plan, so when they're unavailable or circumstances change, I get really sad. I've constructed such a detailed mental picture of what I was expecting, that I find it hard to readjust.

How to Help: advance notice and practice

Most professionals will tell you the best way to help an autistic person deal with change is by giving advance notice to allow them to prepare for an upcoming alternative. As someone on the spectrum, I agree with that 100%. It is much easier to develop alternative mental images when you aren't dealing with the devastation of a shattered picture.

I'm often asked to provide a specific recommendation about the right amount of advance notice. Here's my answer: it is usually best (obviously, with some exceptions) to give autistic individuals as much notice about an upcoming change *as would be helpful to them*. May I pause a moment to emphasize that I did *not* say "Give as much notice as possible?" Remember that lots of autistic people have co-occurring anxiety disorders. Statistically, most of us do, resulting from other disabilities in addition to autism. Knowing about minor changes months or weeks in advance may only increase the level of anxiety. Getting to know the "sweet spot" for advance notice of change will depend on the individual.

Like we've discussed earlier, practice is a great starting point for building skills—including the ability to tolerate change. It is easy for families, educators, and even therapists to become too reliant on routines because they know routines are comfortable for the autistic people they want to support. However, high levels of rigidity aren't comfortable—or sustainable. So what's the answer?

I suggest building routines (with input from the autistic person to the greatest extent possible) that inherently incorporate a certain amount of flexibility by including *categories* of activities rather than one specific activity. For example, the routine might include playing a game (rather than playing Uno), getting a snack (rather than eating M&Ms), and going for a walk (rather than walking to the park). Of course, this strategy works only if you actually rotate through various options. I know from experience that the process can require persistence and patience, but an increased ability to tolerate change is worth the effort.

Remember those Fisher Price figures? Another option for practicing change is some role play that includes scenarios in which unexpected changes occur. Again, constructing new mental images is much easier when you are not surrounded by the shards of your shattered expectations!

Unplanned Change: coping with surprises

What happens when we *can't* give notice? That's an important consideration, since unplanned disruption is a regular feature of life nobody gets to control. When an unexpected change occurs, presenting the information in a concise and direct way, along with explaining why the change is necessary, will often be the most helpful. Scary situations become less scary when we understand what's happening and why.

This is where the power of choice comes in. Giving people choices, even if the choices seem small, can return the feeling of control and help them create a new image, piece by piece. When I work with clients, I follow a specific format. If they show signs of being upset as the result of a request I can't grant, I'll give an empathy statement to show that I understand what they want and how they feel. This could sound like, "I know you really wanted [fill in blank]. I'm really sorry."

Next, I'll tell them when or how they can have their request. If you think about it, when we are told "No," most often it doesn't mean never. Most of the time "No" just means "Not right now." Saying something like, "That would be a great idea for when the sun is out" tells the person under which conditions they can have or do what they want. I'll often provide a visual to confirm that I understand the request and that I plan to help them follow up on it at another time. This might be just writing down the request for them to see or taking a picture of the activity they wanted. I might say, "Let's write this idea on a sticky note so we don't forget about it."

Last, I'll remind them of what the current available options are to support them in choosing an alternative. This could sound like, "Right now, we can read a book or play in the backyard." Again, this may require patience on your part. Stay aware they may need time to process their disappointment, and know they may package it as anger!

It is worth noting again that choice-making is a skill that not everyone has. If that is the case, you may have to make a guess at a choice, try it, and be prepared to pivot if it is not working. You cannot simply force a person to make a choice if that's beyond the person's ability.

I often hear from people that they don't have any choices to offer. I suggest that if you don't have a choice about *what* needs to happen, you consider the *how, who, when,* and *where.* Try offering one of these options:

- On the floor or at the table?

- In the living room or while we walk?

- You first or me first?

- Together or by yourself?

- The big one or the little one?

- Fast or slow?

- Silly or serious?

- Loud or quiet?

If you need more ideas, read *Green Eggs and Ham*!

(Un) Happy Holidays: our annual disruption dilemma

In some cases, we can expect some change well enough actually to plan for it. So, let's talk about the dreaded … I mean "happy!" … holidays that keep popping up throughout the year, year after year, disrupting everyone's routines.

School, therapy, or work schedules change. Company arrives. Travel might be necessary. Crazy new foods are served. Unfamiliar clothes are pulled out. Holiday events bombard our schedules left and right. This combination of factors can be a hard and scary time for any autistic person, and the stress levels will be correspondingly higher for individuals with less understanding of the entire concept of *holiday*. They might understand nothing at all about Thanksgiving, Christmas, or summer vacation. All they know is that the routine which normally provides comfort and helps them understand what to expect has vanished. Every day looks different and they do not know how to anticipate what's next.

Depending on communication ability and personal preference, here are some tips for helping them cope.

- Use a calendar to count down the days.

- Incorporate a visual schedule that keeps track of progress throughout the day.

- Write or describe what activities will take place.

- Always have (and communicate) an alternative option for decompressing.

- Create opportunities for people of all abilities to contribute to holiday celebrations (hanging a decoration, serving a drink, delivering a present).

- Bring tools (fidget toys, whiteboard and markers for quick communication, favorite puzzle) to stay regulated and relaxed.

- Talk to friends and family about autism and how to engage with this particular person

- Take frequent breaks!

- Avoid holiday clothing that is itchy or uncomfortable.

- Try to incorporate a special interest into the event. If you get to talk about your horrible boss or share pictures of your children, they should get to share a Google search of horse paws or discuss train schedules.

- It's okay to say "no thanks" if someone makes a request that creates challenges. You don't have to accept a hug. You don't have to stay late. You don't have to try foods.

Above all, don't underestimate the impact of changed routines at holiday times. My parents tried hard to head off problems before they started. Mom used to start me on a game plan for casual family gatherings well in advance of all holidays. To me, at that time, I called it getting in "pre-trouble." Pre-trouble happens when your parents sit you down before the event and tell you to "Behave; have a good attitude; and use your manners." They explain at length why you should do those things and what would happen if you don't. While I had every intention of "behaving, having a good attitude, and using my manners" (whatever those things actually meant), we all knew that this was just the first of at least three different lectures I'd be receiving that day.

I could usually keep it together for a few hours, but eventually I started giving off the warning signs that time was running out: running around, making noise, and arguing with adults' instructions. As those behaviors escalated—and the resulting family commentary drifted from "kids just being kids" to "what is *wrong* with that kid?"—I found myself being abruptly removed from the room.

Looking back, I realize nothing was abrupt about it. I was asked to settle down or be quiet plenty of times. They may have even attempted to redirect me to something more acceptable. When (1) I didn't respond correctly and (2) others were sick of me, I can remember my dad picking me up and carrying me like a sack of potatoes to the next room. My parents didn't do spanking, at least not that I can remember. So when we got to the next room, I'd get plopped down so that I could receive the second in the series of "Behave; have a good attitude; and use your manners" lectures.

These lectures could've been considered effective if they had resulted in improvement in my behavior at future family gatherings … but they didn't, at least not for several years. Instead, I just became keenly aware of what I was in those situations—rude, hyper, and occasionally disrespectful. As a result, you may correctly assume I didn't become a huge fan of holiday-themed family get-togethers.

Later in my adolescence, the "hyperness" quieted down in the presence of extended family, but it was unfortunately replaced with a lot of rudeness. To be clear, this term was not necessarily a mischaracterization of my behavior, though it certainly never represented my intentions at the moment. From overly direct questions, like "Oh my god, what's wrong with your eye? Why is it so red and puffy?" to inflammatory comments about politics and religion, I continued to find new ways to get myself in trouble (pre-trouble, mid-trouble, and post-trouble) with family over the holidays.

As an adult, I'd be lying to you if I said pre-trouble doesn't happen anymore, because it does, but now it takes a different form. Most recently, it still comes with "be friendly, try to smile, and be polite" but the if/then statements have evolved a bit. As a child it was "If you can't have a good attitude, then we will have to step outside until everyone else is done." These days it's more like "If you could be friendly with Aunt B and C, then it would really mean a lot to me." The other positive change in pre-trouble as the result of adulthood has been adding negotiated time limits and designated alternatives. "After you stay at Grammy's house for a couple of hours, and everyone has finished eating, you can drive back to our house if you'd like to do something else." And one of my favorites: "If someone says something crazy, we can talk about it in the car, but not while we're still with them."

Arguably these things could've been made available to me as a child as well, but, as they say, "live and learn." While certain modifications may seem like the obvious way to go, sometimes we come to those conclusions only after accumulating experience in the other direction first. Meanwhile, please remember that total changes in your routine, unusual gatherings, widely varied food, and rowdy conversation with many relatives might be coveted, fun, and exciting for some. For us autistic people? Not so much.

Chapter 9

Repetitive Actions: Insights from Inside

My best fidget toys have names. Mouth Slug. Eleanor Slugsevelt. Dr. Greg Hanley (named for an inspirational clinician). And let's not forget He Comes In Skunk (for the squishy rubber dog who arrived in my life wearing a skunk costume). When I'm looking for a fidget, I'm usually searching for ones that "have a good shake." I appreciate a selection of textures and weights but usually prefer smaller objects that fit in my pockets.

As an adult who still *names* her favorite items, I think the desire to care for one's belongings isn't a big leap. As a result, I generally don't like to share my fidgets. I can make recommendations all day, and I'll even let you try it—but I want it back within a few minutes!

When I work with kids, I bring only the fidgets I wouldn't mind sharing and wouldn't be upset if they were broken or lost. I reserve the special ones for when I'm at home or working around adults. That said, one of the best parts of working at a school where *all* the kids are on the spectrum is they don't usually find it noteworthy or different when an adult walks in holding a fun fidget toy. The kids usually have their own and aren't interested in mine. This is all because they already know what we need to talk about next: repetitive movements are a core feature of autism.

Stimming: why we do it

While most people associate repetitive behavior with autism, *everyone* stims! Including you, whoever you may be. *Stimming*, shorthand for self-stimulatory behavior, is more formally known as stereotypy. The technical definition is repetition of physical movements, sounds, words, or moving objects. You and I and everyone else do stimming. The difference between your stimming and mine is intensity and quantity. And, I have to say, I think the quality of mine is likely better than yours (unless you are also autistic)! For an autistic person, stimming might become so intense and frequent that it interferes with needed communication, skill-building, or even physical safety. Such high levels of stimming, referred to as "stereotyped or repetitive motor movements, use of objects, or speech," is part of the DSM-5 diagnostic criteria.

Stimming as a neurotypical person might be a matter of clicking a pen, bouncing your leg, humming a tune, or biting your nails. Stimming as an autistic person could look like pacing, shaking objects, finger flicking, or rocking. Why do people do this? Easy answer. People stim because it feels good. It can help us regulate stress and other emotions. Autistic people might stim more than most because besides helping us regulate our emotions, it can help us process sensory input or think through a complicated sequence.

There is much debate about when—or if—to deflect stimming. Answers are complex and highly individualized, but a few basic principles can help us sort through options and priorities.

Most importantly, a stim that is physically harmful is a different discussion from something that isn't hurting anyone. If a child stims by biting his own hand or banging her head on the wall, you may need a medical evaluation. A self-harming stim could be a response to a physical problem you can't see and the person can't explain.

Deciding whether a stim is interfering with skill acquisition is a somewhat different matter. That discussion calls for lots of nuances. In the past, people were far more quick to consider the stim as an interference when it really might have just been unusual. However, sometimes stimming does, in fact, present a barrier to a skill that is, in fact, critical. Think safety, for example. If you are too deep in your stimming to notice ongoing traffic, that can be a problem. If that's what's going on with the autistic person in your life, you'll probably need input from a good therapist.

People (autistic or not) are not always even aware when they're stimming. Remember that time someone in your family yelled at you to stop tapping your fork on the table? You were barely aware you were doing it; you were just trying to concentrate. Similarly, autistic people may not recognize when and if they are stimming. For instance, I've had a habit since childhood that I didn't even recognize as a stim until a therapist pointed it out to me one day near the end of high school. She was helping me fill out some paperwork, which is a task that really irks my soul! Trying both to reduce my stress and to insert small delays, I'd pause between each blank space to shake the pen between my fingers. The therapist saw that the repeated stopping and pen shaking was dragging out the unpleasant process. Tired of waiting all the extra time for me to finish this form, she finally said, "I need you to stop shaking the pen and keep working." For a variety of reasons, paperwork makes my blood boil! When she gave me the directive, I must not have finished shaking out all the anxiety, because my immediate reaction was to fling the pen across the room … one of those accidental impulses I have luckily grown better at controlling. But not always!

At that moment I realized shaking objects was my go-to fidget. For me, it's not about the sound. It's about feeling the rapid shifting of weight in my hands. And no, I can't tell you what that does for me outside generic descriptions like "helps me focus, keeps me calm, reduces anxiety, or just feels good." This episode helped me realize shaking objects had become a stim. I'd been discreetly focusing on whatever objects happened to be around, such as my pen, my necklace, something on my desk, or some part of my clothing. But I didn't see the pattern until someone else pointed it out to me. With this new clarity, I started looking for objects that *like* to be shaken. (Thank you, Eleanor Slugsevelt!) With a whole market of different fidget toys out there, my new self-awareness allowed me to indulge in the stress relief of shaking excellent fidget objects while simultaneously staying on task.

I do feel the need to point out that the occasional autistic person might engage in uninterrupted stimming until they reach such a heightened state they cannot come back down without help. There are certain songs I don't listen to at work, even when wearing my headphones. It would be like attending a rave for one! I know the resulting over-hyped state will not be productive for anyone.

All that to say, keep in mind that purposefully squelching a stim (even assuming you could) might result in a replacement behavior that's even more problematic. It also might cause the autistic person's withdrawal from interaction to the extent they can, simply because you're making life more uncomfortable for them. If a stim is not dangerous and not impeding learning, my advice is either to incorporate it somehow, as described above, or else just get over it. Stims are normal and, in many situations, are extremely useful to autistic people. They can raise or lower sensory input as needed. Stims can help us focus on tasks and manage our emotions.

Perseveration: maggots in my mind

Remember that time your cousin couldn't stop talking about Area 51 even after everyone at the party walked away from him? How about the persistent little problem of replaying in your mind (over and over) that awkward encounter you had with your ex a few months ago? From time to time we all experience the uneasy feeling of being "stuck" on something. This unpleasant phenomenon has a name: *perseveration*. It means getting fixated on a thought, idea, or topic and being unable to mentally or emotionally shift gears.

Perseveration happens when someone engages in needless repetition of words, thoughts, or actions. More technically, it's the continuation of an experience or activity without the appropriate environmental stimulus. This is common in people with disorders (like OCD and anxiety) that affect thought processes. But like so many other factors, perseveration can be particularly challenging for autistic people. Many on the spectrum experience perseveration far more strongly than others. It becomes an issue of scale and intensity.

Perseveration can include repeating the same questions, even if they've already been answered. It can mean insisting on having the same conversation over and over. Someone is perseverating when they can't break away from repetitive thoughts on one topic or can't stop movements such as repeatedly rearranging items. Even more complex, one form of perseveration happens when a person holds onto certain emotions long after the situation that caused those emotions has passed.

Let's distinguish between perseveration and stims. Stims tend to be sensory in nature and usually don't have an additional, non-sensory objective. With stims, the action *itself* meets a need. Perseveration is more complex, targeting something beyond the action or thought. The person stuck in perseveration has a goal to accomplish, but has trouble understanding when the goal has already been met or is impossible.

Stimming is a bit like scratching an itch; perseveration is more like trying to handle your itch by scratching someone else!

Unlike stimming, perseveration usually starts from anxiety. It's associated with feelings of restlessness and worry. That last part is what makes it different from our special interests, which we will discuss later.

Perseveration can ruin my day and probably yours, too. When I think about preservation, I think about what might happen if you scraped your knee back in the 1700s, pre-antibiotics. A wound might end up getting full of maggots that would eat away from the inside until it healed (or you died from infection!). Sometimes my perseverative thoughts just eat my soul until the wound heals over, which can take a lot of time.

So, what can you do when the maggots set in? Again, everyone occasionally experiences having something "stuck in your head." But autistic people often experience this problem at higher rates and may need the support of another person to get ourselves unstuck. Whether perseveration is your own struggle or happening to someone you're trying to assist, how do you change it?

The most immediate strategy is redirection. This won't stop perseveration from happening again in the future, but it may provide some short-term relief. In my experience, the most helpful redirection is to engage in activities that require a certain amount of movement, concentration, or both. This strategy has two parts.

First, set a timer. Allow the person to continue perseverating for the duration of the timer, which can include talking through thoughts, allowing space for repetition, answering questions, or journaling the repetitive thoughts. When the timer goes off, we go to the second step of picking an activity, ideally one that requires movement and concentration.

- Take a walk or run.

- Stretch in certain poses.

- Read a book.

- Do a puzzle.

- Do a craft.

- Write a story.

- Play a board game.

- Listen to music.

Everyone will need something different, but any activity that requires a person to move and concentrate should be helpful. Your person will probably resist this strategy, so you shouldn't expect immediate cooperation. Don't give up too easily. Beyond that, if the autistic person in your life has the communicative ability to discuss this with you, try to find out what might be the easiest and most attractive way to help them get unstuck. If they can't tell you, you're going to face a process of trial and error.

In the interest of full disclosure, I have to point out that sometimes a timer and a list of choices is just not going to get the job done. For some, perseverative thoughts can focus on some philosophical point or world-crisis problem that can't be solved very well by any kind of redirection. Frankly, that happens to me quite often, and I have named the situation *intellectual terrorism*. The only factor that ever helps me work through it is a chance to talk the problem through on an intellectual level with someone whose opinion I already trust and have high confidence in. If we can come to some sort of conclusion, well, sure, that helps. But if it's not a solvable problem, then I'm having a true experience of "It sucks to be me," and I'm just going to have to deal with the repetitive thoughts. If your response to such a conclusion is, "Well, Kaelynn, that's just not very helpful!" then I say back that it might at least help you understand what's going on for the autistic person in your life—what their challenges look like and what they're trying to cope with while the rest of the world goes about other business!

Scripting: borrowed language

I don't remember using scripting when I was a kid. But my mom sure remembers my having the entire dialogue of *The Lion King* memorized, scene by scene, and how I often used the movie structure to fill in any perceived social gaps—including my own boredom with my immediate company. *Scripting* is memorizing and repeating words or phrases from any wide variety of sources. Scripting can come from videos, TV shows, or conversations with others.

In my experience, scripting can serve two functions. The first is an attempt to self-soothe. Repeating familiar scripts can bring feelings of comfort (similar to the routines we discussed earlier). The second is to compensate for language deficits. For instance, if a person has difficulty asking others for help, they may pull a phrase from a favorite TV show and recite "Help is on the way!"

Of course, non-autistic people also quote favorite lines, with repetition frequently happening whenever a particular script is popular. So my version of scripting—answering a question or maybe responding to a funny situation with a quote from a well-known movie—doesn't stand out as unusual.

For others, however, the script may seem odd because it is devoid of known context. But even though *you* might not recognize the context, the script may hold meaning for the autistic person. Those words may reflect needs or desires. Or they might show a need for comfort and are a strong cue that someone is anxious or stressed. For instance, when my friend Colby encounters a stressful situation, his script is "Tweak me achin' nose!" which comes from a *Mary Poppins* lyric. Those of us around him have learned that it means he feels stressed, and it can be a valid communication for us to help him cope. Many of our speech and language pathologist friends—or parents with children in speech therapy—will recognize scripting as part of the Gestalt language development process. It's long been observed in the autistic experience and can have much communication value on its own, whether or not the autistic person is ever able to self-generate more complex sentences. If you are a parent/caregiver/friend of a person who uses scripts for communication or an autistic person who is able to do so, I suggest keeping a handbook of translations for others to facilitate their understanding.

Chapter 10

Sensory Distortion: Do You Hear What I Hear? (Nope)

No sounds ever actually stab me in the ear holes, but sometimes it really does feel like it! One day I tried to explain to my mom why autistic people can be sensitive to loud noises. We were sitting in a restaurant. I was considering putting on my headphones because I was hungry and grumpy and the restaurant was loud. Any one of those three factors all by itself could create a significant challenge for me. All three together were compounding each other, creating the classic vicious circle, and pushing me toward sensory overload. You see, I share a challenge with most other autistic people. The area of the brain where I'm supposed to perceive sensation crosses over to where I perceive pain. In short, my brain is misfiring and interpreting noise as pain. My hearing is not, in reality, more acute than other people's hearing. But my brain is not interpreting noise correctly. It hurts!

Similar misfires can be true for all senses of any autistic person. It's not our actual ability to smell, touch, taste, hear, or see that's heightened. Rather, it's our brain's *interpretation* of those senses that's sometimes tuned differently from that of most neurotypical people. Have you heard different people say that "Autistic people are wired differently?" This is part of what they mean.

Avoiders and Seekers: individualized experience

Sometimes a given signal or sensation may not even register for most humans, but because of the autistic brain's misinterpretation, the same signal might be painful or overwhelming for some of us. A noise might not be just loud—it might actually be painful to the ears. A tap may feel like a slap. A hole in a sock may rub down to our very last nerve.

These heightened sensitivities can result in the need to muffle the impact in some way—to be a sensory avoider. Conversely, sometimes autistic people's bodies require more input, making them sensory seekers. Like everything else, this is highly individualized, subject to change based on the conditions the person is experiencing at any given time. To be clear, a person can be both a seeker and an avoider, depending on many factors. The critical consideration is that the brain and neurons of an autistic person often report sensory input as far higher or lower than what unaffected people experience. To make matters even more complex, such distorted neurological processing is not consistent. Not only does it vary by individual, but it can vary day to day for the same person.

I'm usually a sensory avoider. I often use headphones and earplugs to reduce sound. When outside, I wear sunglasses. When inside, I avoid overhead lights if possible because they're too bright. However, there are times, especially when I haven't exercised recently, when I seek stimulation. This might be a matter of playing loud music, running around the house, and singing along to the most obnoxious SpongeBob trap music I can find. Bonus points if my roommates yell at me to stop.

An autistic person who starts a disruptive behavior might be seeking sensory stimulation. Even if that particular behavior can't be tolerated, it's still important to ensure the sensory need gets met. Of course, ideally we want the need to get met with activities that don't get on everyone else's nerves or cause physical danger. To accomplish that, we have to identify the sensation they're seeking. Then we attempt to replicate the sensation somehow that's safe, sanitary, and socially acceptable. For example, playing with certain food substances or shaving cream can be a good alternative to fecal smearing. Maybe I have found the one statement that everybody can agree on!

Controlling the Equation: advocacy plus action

So how do we address this combination of varying challenges? It's not a simple answer, any more than it is a simple problem. My years as a therapist have taught me that people don't always take the easiest route to a solution. They're more likely, for example, to ask others to stop talking than they are to go to a different room. I think it's important to teach any possible strategies for people to change their *own* behavior to regulate sensory input. So key moves will be (1) identifying the sensory need, whether more or less of any particular stimulus, and (2) establishing access to a safe means of obtaining it with the least possible disruption to others.

That's definitely not to say that autistic people shouldn't advocate for their needs to others! Or that parents or friends of autistic people shouldn't try to advocate for them in appropriate ways—asking for reduced TV volume, removing a scented candle from the table, or locating a seat in the uncrowded section of a movie theater. But the bottom line? We usually don't get to decide what others do, but we can control what *we* do. When faced with sensory problems, the option with the greatest leverage will usually be for the autistic person to generate solutions that are within their own control. For instance, if someone is being too loud, you might be able to ask them to quiet down. But what if they don't? If not, there's more immediate effect—and control—in putting on headphones or going to another room. Especially because individual needs fluctuate, it's important for both seekers and avoiders to learn a variety of healthy ways to get what they need. The same noise that didn't bother you last week might bother you a lot this week. We can't expect other people to know when that happens. When the situation changes, it's often quickest and most effective to make the necessary sensory changes ourselves rather than asking someone to do it for us.

Reading the Clues: when self-advocacy isn't obvious

For older children and adults, whether or not they can use spoken language, advocating for sensory needs can be quite complex. Ironically, despite having autism (you know, the disorder that complicates communication?), I spoke early at eight months. And I haven't shut up since. I have words to fill whole days. Don't like my words? I have different ones! Just ask and I'll be happy to demonstrate.

However.

Other autistic people are not always so lucky. They can't just change their wording if it doesn't come out right the first time. In fact, many can't even "word" to begin with. Because of this, I'd like to offer you some translations from my own perspective. Some autistic people can't say: "I need sensory pressure right now." Instead, they might tense up their muscles …. Or roll around on the floor …. Or insist on wearing a jacket with the hood pulled all the way up. Someone might not have the language or comfort level to say "I feel overstimulated!" They might try to address their need by pacing in circles or hiding under a table.

Parents and friends, please note that often the cues are not obvious. Even as a seasoned therapist who has sensory issues herself, I am not always aware when my clients need sensory regulation. I would expect my language-abled clients to verbalize that something sounds too loud or to cover their ears with their hands. However, sometimes that expression of feeling "off" looks like contributing to the chaos of the environment by being too much themselves—either being extra loud or overly rambunctious. Of course, sometimes they may not be bothered at all but are unconsciously ramping up to match what is going on.

So this is tricky! If you can ask your person what they need and they can reliably answer, great. But I think this situation is very rare. More often, they may not realize what they need—which will require some building of both awareness and coping skills. With a nonspeaking person, for instance, you might work with them to create a visual menu containing pictures of the various ways they can safely seek or avoid a particular sensation. Seeing which options are available can help them make a choice and communicate that choice to someone who can assist them.

Keep in mind that someone on the spectrum might not have the ability to give more detail when asked for clarification. Instead, they get defensive … louder … or even combative. Some of us don't know how to say "I'm distressed that you don't understand me, because I don't have other words to explain it any better."

Always remember that autistic people trying to meet a sensory need don't necessarily default to a method that's palatable for others. Sometimes it's not even understandable by other people. If you're able to help autistic people advocate for themselves, watch for moments similar to what's described here. Behaviors that might initially look like rampant acting out can mean something else entirely. Such moments certainly do not feel like self-advocacy, but they're tremendously important because they're showing you where self-advocacy is needed most! And hopefully will lead to teaching moments that provide more reliable ways to advocate for the sensory input that is needed.

Chapter 11

Perceptions and Perspectives: Same World, Different Lens

My eight-year-old autistic client lied to me, and I congratulated him. Why? Autistic people can struggle with comparing the information they know with what information other people know—and with when and how to fill in the gaps. For example, you come to visit me from out of town. While driving us to lunch at my favorite restaurant, you miss a turn. In order for me to understand why you drove past it, I'd need to realize that just because *I* know where the turn is doesn't necessarily mean *you* do. For you also to have that same information about the turn, you'd need to be told. Children typically start figuring this out around the age of three—that they might have information you don't. As a result, that's often when they start intentionally lying. I'd been working on this concept of *knowing* with my eight-year-old client for several weeks. When I collected him from his regular class to go to therapy, he told me he needed to finish eating. I believed him! He said I needed to watch him unzip his lunch box. Then he started laughing hysterically when he revealed the container was empty. "Tricked you!" he said with great satisfaction. I congratulated him because he understood I didn't know he'd already eaten all his food, since I hadn't been at the cafeteria with him.

Theory of Mind: understanding different points of view

Learning to understand another person's point of view is a recognized childhood development milestone. It starts with what I just described:

understanding that not everyone has the same information. Then it gets more complicated through learning that someone might have thoughts that are different from your own. In my line of work, we refer to this as *theory of mind,* meaning a person can assign meaning to and (to some extent) understand someone else's state of mind when it's different from their own. This recognition of interpersonal difference forms the foundation for being able to predict and interpret others' behaviors. In more common terms, the ability is what's often just called understanding a different perspective.

Any realistic understanding of autism will have to include recognition that not only is theory of mind, the tuning-in, usually quite delayed, but also that its application is challenging throughout the autistic person's life.

Now, sure, all people can be resistant to seeing life from a different perspective. Want a real-life, immediate example? Just look around you at this country's ultra-polarized political climate! But please understand: autistic people often have an even harder time than most others. Why such a difference? As with so many autism concerns, the problem becomes one of scale and intensity. Several common characteristics of autism intersect here, and each plays a role. One big factor would be what we've discussed in the previous chapter about differences in how our brains process sensory information. Probably almost all readers have heard the snarky saying people use when they're overwhelmed with too many tasks, "Yeah, I have too many tabs open!" They don't mean their computers, of course, but their brains. For an autistic person, a disagreeable sensory issue, too much or too little, can be like those tabs. The problem isn't necessarily about too many tabs, but when That Certain One opens up, it dominates all the others, because, for instance, it has really loud music that won't let you focus on the rest. That's overly simplified, but it still illustrates the difference between an autistic brain and a neurotypical brain. That One Thing—that pesky tab—makes all the difference to their world, but they may or may not ever understand that the problem is not the same for everyone else. What might be an unpleasant odor to most could give the autistic person a sense of near suffocation. A disagreeable taste or a relatively normal sound might cause physical pain to an autistic kid. So for accurate interpersonal interaction, the person with autism must learn not only to distinguish *what* is on the other person's mind, but also to understand that the like, dislike, or sensation is often—maybe even usually—nowhere near as intense as their own.

So, circling back to the challenges of understanding someone else's point of view, the variations in sensory perception pile one issue on top of another. Think about the kind of statements many of us have heard from the autistic people in our lives (or maybe even made ourselves). "He was being mean when he told me that I needed to follow that direction." "She slammed that door loudly just to bother me." "They hit me when they walked past me." When you are overly sensitive to sound, it's easy to perceive that someone yelled at you when they might have just changed their tone of voice. When you're sensitive to touch, a tap could feel like a shove.

Consider one of my autistic client's recent announcements that his classmate often paces near his desk "to annoy him." I acknowledge to my student that it's possible his interpretation might be right, but then explain some other reasons the classmate might be pacing. "They might be trying to get rid of excess energy" or "He might be feeling nervous." Or both: "Maybe he had extra energy to get out because he was nervous about something."

Perceiving different versions of the same events can certainly add to conflict, if not itself cause conflict. What's critical to understand in matters of perception is that no one is necessarily wrong. You may also need to play detective and source your information from other people who witnessed the events or who are familiar with the situation. Don't presume your friend's or child's perspective is wrong, but try to gather alternatives to provide balance. It may take quite a lot of patient work and explanation to help someone understand that alternative points of view exist.

Rudeness: when directness crosses the line

I've explained how autistic people are almost automatically more direct because of how our brains work. But in social settings, when you line up directness beside all those unwritten social rules, we can quickly arrive at a brand new area of misunderstanding: rudeness. When autistic people interact with neurotypical people, a frequent point of confusion is the gray area where directness starts getting perceived as rudeness. When I was growing up, because of my autism I made more social mistakes than other kids my age, which meant adults often described my behavior as rude. Lots of teens are rude. It's in their job description. And while that might be the case, I seemed to get called out more than most! It reached the point where I was sometimes afraid of new situations, not just because of their uncertainty but also because I was afraid others would see that I was rude. Rudeness became a piece of who I was, and it was a part I was ashamed of.

When I was young, others often worded their feedback about my behavior as "That was rude." Or they might say "You're being rude." They might even say "You *are* rude." The effects of all those statements varied only in intensity. In time, I believed there was something inherently offensive about my personal style of interaction. I never intended to be rude. In fact, from my perspective, I was attempting to be the opposite. There's something seriously disorienting about having very clear intentions and personal values, yet being perceived by those around you as anything but what you'd hoped to show. For me, an increased number of social mistakes resulted in increased negative feedback from adults, but while teachers and therapists were quick to provide this behavioral feedback, they rarely told me what to do instead!

All I heard was "That's rude," so I didn't know specifically what needed to be changed. But if they had said, "When you want an answer to a personal question, ask it this way ...." I could have adjusted my behavior. Social feedback is best when it's more actionable and less descriptive.

Rude or not rude? That depends. Autistic people have a hard time identifying unwritten social rules. If they can't identify them, then they can't follow them either. Too often, nobody takes the time to teach us about these cultural rules we're all expected magically to absorb, know, and follow. Knowing how to adapt our behavior correctly to different contexts makes the difference between having smooth social interactions and having significant interpersonal challenges.

Common struggles include knowing:

- how much personal information is appropriate to share with acquaintances,

- how to navigate the social niceties of varying situations, and

- how to change our behaviors to fit social hierarchies.

Consider my 20-year-old client, who needed my help with improving conversational skills. Teaching someone conversational give-and-take requires setting a good example, which required me to show genuine interest in the things he cared about. Did I really want to know more about weather patterns, local trains, and *Family Guy* compilations on *YouTube*? Not even a little bit. But to get his agreement to work on conversational skills, I had to show interest in his preferred topics.

Once he realized my willingness to discuss his favorite topics, this client would periodically ask if we could date. His query had merit when he looked at the evidence in front of him. He and I were close in age, we had shared areas of knowledge surrounding the weather, and both of us giggled at politically incorrect jokes on *Family Guy*. What more could you want in a romantic relationship?

Repeatedly declining his dating invitation didn't get me anywhere. Finally, I made a slide presentation titled *Why Clients Can't Date Helpers*. I counted myself in the community helpers category. I taught him that helpers included nurses, respite workers, teachers, counselors, and therapists. I explained that these types of community helpers get paid to perform duties for their clients. He needed lots of clarifications about friends and family members who might also give help, but they're not paid to do so.

Key take-away? He needed to learn that it was inappropriate for a helper who was getting paid to date a client. That might seem obvious to many, but it was not to him. He misunderstood the social rules around dating, which resulted in a mildly uncomfortable discussion. However, that same misunderstanding in a different setting could have a more punitive outcome. Frankly, it's best for all involved that this situation played out in a therapeutic setting rather than in the workplace or out in the community.

The so-called social norms that govern much of life are usually more basic than that lengthy example. But not always! What seems so obvious to many might need to be boiled down into a structured, simplified single statement. A social norm needs to be reduced to a specifically articulated sentence, complete with exact rationale. That's frequently the only way an autistic person is going to understand.

So, we can often avert misunderstanding by providing the autistic person enough information and practice. But as you seek to understand the broader world of autism, please keep in mind that many autistic people have no such luxury. They might be children without adequate support or therapy. They might be undiagnosed adults. Without direct, adequate teaching about these social norms, autistic people can have enormous trouble navigating our current society. Repeated misunderstandings or "offenses", as they're sometimes called, can get autistic people into a lot of trouble. Not only can social misunderstandings result in termination from a job, but they also can escalate into a police interaction or even incarceration. According to a 2001 FBI bulletin, people with developmental disabilities—which includes the autism diagnosis—are seven times more likely to have police encounters than the general population (Debbaudt and Rothman 2001). They are also statistically more likely to be victims of a violent crime (Trundle 2023). Far too many police departments don't exactly have a good reputation for making friends. I bet you could guess that police interactions with autistic people don't always have happy endings. On the bright side, more police departments than ever before now do training on how to recognize and deal with autism. I hope that trend continues. Unfortunately, it is still far too common that law enforcement officers struggle to identify who we are.

However, as individuals, we want to be as socially proactive as possible. With that goal in mind, please remember that sometimes, teaching someone when, where, or with whom they *can* do something will be far more productive than any other action. Educators, therapists, and families, here's your clearly articulated statement from me: next time you see someone getting frustrated at hearing, over and over, that what they're doing is wrong, show them how they can be *right!*

Reading the Rooms: when the lights go low it's harder for us

Sometimes, being right is more about your audience than content. Many autistic people struggle with selecting the correct conversational audience. You wouldn't tell a sexually oriented joke to your boss or your grandma. The cashier at the grocery store doesn't need to hear about your diarrhea. Most acquaintances don't want to be insulted, even playfully. Obviously, there's some nuance to such situations, but you get my point. People on the spectrum struggle to "read the room," and sometimes get themselves in trouble for something they said, even if they definitely did not mean any harm.

Reading rooms? It's a common term. But it can be really tricky for autistic people. Despite having autism, I like to think that my ability to read a room is at least sufficient for keeping me out of trouble. Maybe you were born knowing how to read body language and adjust your behavior to differing contexts, but I had to learn how to do those things. Now that I've learned, I have to approach such things with much deliberate thought and focus. I have to consider, evaluate, and decide how to act. Most people get automatic transmission on their emotional navigation system. I get the manual version: stick shift, clutch, and about 15 gears. Can I do it? Usually. But it's quite a different process from how most do so in the background of their minds without needing conscious focus.

So, yes, I can read a room so long as the room isn't being shady. If the "lights are on," meaning that people are genuine in their interactions, I do pretty well. However, I don't always notice when the lights go down … that is, when people hide their true intentions behind behavior that appears friendly.

I don't have many work friends so when a co-worker invited me to eat lunch with them one day, I jumped at the chance. In between bites of my tuna sandwich, they kept asking me about sensitive work-related things, information about my finances, and other things that they weren't really supposed to know. Assuming they were just taking an interest in me, I thought a friendship was finally being formed! Not long afterward, my supervisor sat me down and told me I needed to be careful about who I gave private information to. So while I can read a room, when "the lights go low," my read isn't always accurate. This is just one of the many joys of autism.

In my case, I needed help from my supervisor to understand my audience. That just because someone asked such questions didn't mean I should automatically answer.

Divulging too much personal information might seem far removed from the young man who struggled to understand why helpers can't date clients. But at its root, it's the same difficulty with reading that room, and that's what needs to be addressed.

When someone is really motivated to engage in a particular behavior, it's helpful to give them information about who would be the right folks to have in the room. For example, one of my middle school clients thoroughly enjoyed being funny, but kept getting in trouble for sharing off-color humor out loud in the middle of his classroom that was full of teachers and therapists. Instead of trying to insist that, "No, you can never tell those jokes at school, no matter how funny they are," I needed to teach him the appropriate audience for those kinds of jokes. Together we came up with some funny jokes and statements on different topics, and we made a list of who would think each joke was funny … plus a few more lists of those who would not think so!

Not long after making the lists, he explained to me how he told a bathroom humor joke to a classmate, how the classmate laughed, and that he didn't get in trouble from the teacher—because he told the classmate and not the teacher!

It bears repeating: you might have better luck teaching someone when and how they can do something rather than when they can't. The negative side of effort to change a behavior can cause emotional responding, making it harder to learn a new skill.

While that example is about defining the appropriate when and how for a child, trust me, the same principle applies to considerably more grown-up scenarios. Like one of mine!

Yeah, I might look like I'd be really nice to talk to, but when I first started working full time I was a full-fledged menace of inappropriate comments. I knew how to make conversation. I knew if I asked about my co-workers' weekend plans, they'd tell me. But who has time for all that? I didn't! I mean, it's not *my* fault that other people's mistakes were just more intellectually stimulating to talk about than where they were going for drinks! But it turns out that co-workers don't necessarily appreciate commentary on how they could get better at their jobs. So, probably tired of my nonsense and maybe tired of getting complaints, my supervisor made me a deal. I could text her all of my rude thoughts, as long as I didn't say them out loud. In return, she promised to give some sort of response, even if all she could send was a string of empathetic emojis. A few months of keeping this arrangement resulted in two things. First, increased self-awareness! Slowing down to type your thoughts, because you might get in trouble for saying the wrong ones out loud, really forces you to think before you speak. Second, improvement in my workplace relationships! Being more thoughtful about what came out of my mouth gave me space to have more conventional interactions … even if it was under the threat of punishment. And let's not forget the third benefit: it kept me from getting fired while I was still learning to do the job! Even for myself, working on far more advanced skills than my 11-year-old client with the bathroom humor, learning to understand more about when and where my comments were acceptable, started me down the road of better understanding complex social barriers and how to remove them.

Special Interests: all or nothing

I have an autism-fueled passion for decorative birds, like the ones who stand in department stores in rows of approximately 500 at Christmas. I want them all. I can take one look at the little dude in the middle row and understand his name is Tristan. He lives in a little burg south of me and

drives a truck. And he simply must come home with me. Possibly 20 more of his friends should also come. Did I mention passion? For that matter, I'm intensely interested in birds in general, everything from their calls to their flight patterns. It's similar when it comes to dogs. I can name more dog breeds than some encyclopedias, and I can almost always tell you—on sight—which one just trotted by.

Butterflies? Not so much. Other people might barely notice them, or not feel one way or the other about them if they do notice. Me? Nope! Pretty at a distance, but one of my strongest freak-out moments in recent history was finding myself trapped in a cage at a science park with hundreds of them. As a kid, I wasn't just so-so about all my sister's Barbie dolls and princess costumes. I despised them. My take? Get this stupid stuff out of my face! I had a near-allergic reaction to all matters involving girly pink.

Neutral is a word just not often found in my brain, which leads us into discussion about what's commonly known in autism circles as *big feelings*. Whether those big feelings manifest as special interests or as especially intense emotions, they can be a really different perspective from what neurotypical people experience. The better you understand that and the more you can keep it in mind, the less chance there will be of a mental, practical, or social disconnect.

We all have special interests, hobbies, and topics we love. But again, autism tends to create "extra" in focus. Autistic people often have special interests at an intensity and scale others aren't prepared for. Before I had vocabulary to describe the phenomenon of autistic special interests, I used to refer to my own interests as obsessions. As a child, I didn't know anyone else who felt the same passion I did for birdwatching, training dogs, or *The Lion King*. I was painfully aware how intensely I focused on certain things, and how those things didn't align with my peers' interests. In times of frustration I used to say to my mom, "I wish I could change my obsession!"

Especially when I was very young, substituting the word *specialized* for *obsessive* would have helped me a lot. Being obsessive is typically considered unhealthy, but being specialized is unique and noteworthy! Understanding that distinction could have saved gigantic pieces of my self-esteem. My self-perception kept getting crushed when I was too passionate about my special interests around other kids. My mom remembers even better than I do how disappointed I was when friends failed to appreciate the 1,001 things I could tell them about my dog, Sabrina. About her work as a service dog. About her breed. Her training. Her history. How helpful her work was to me. I was fascinated and had major struggles to understand why they were not.

Professionals used to see only negatives in autistic special interests, but today we understand their value. Even if those interests can't be turned into a career, they still bring the person an immense amount of joy! Special interests can help us connect with others. Many people on the spectrum love to share their passions with anyone willing to learn. Granted, we may need some of that direct help in knowing when the willingness is slipping away due to our over-enthusiastic sharing.

That said, it's important to keep in mind that repetition of a particular topic doesn't always mean it's an actual special interest! Depending on an autistic person's age, ability to communicate, level of experience, and level of anxiety in any social situation, bringing up a certain topic over and over might not mean someone especially likes that topic at all. The repetition might highlight other factors to which you need to pay attention.

For starters, not everybody has special interests! Usually the younger a person is, the less quickly we should assume anything is a special interest. What someone persistently talks about might be because their limited vocabulary can't keep up with the desire for more social connection. If words are limited, what else is there to say? A narrow range of topics might mean only that a child needs exposure to a larger variety. If she's barely seven years old, she can't possibly be aware of all the alternatives to what she's seen and heard about so far. Society can be far too quick to assume that all autistic people are going to be obsessed with a particular topic. Even if a child tells you they "like squirrels best," I advise caution. What if what they really like best might turn out to be polar bears, but they haven't seen one yet? We can move too quickly to planning career goals for a little kid when they can't yet know whether they might want to do other things more. As always, there's a certain amount of truth here for all children, autistic and neurotypical. But I see far too many parents jumping to conclusions. A child who's maybe only recently gained some language skill is often delighted to share with others. Nobody should interpret the very first thing he's learned to talk about as his major area of interest. Maybe it will become that. Or maybe it won't. It's better for everyone if the kids have ongoing exposure to new and other potentially more interesting things so they can choose for themselves.

Lack of exposure also becomes a limiting factor for those with more profound autism. When someone usually appears disinterested in the environment, we're quick to pounce on any glimmer of attention. That glimmer can too quickly get labeled as a special interest, pushing families, educators, and therapists inadvertently to focus so much on that perceived interest that other options don't get explored.

To sum it up, you can't order if you haven't seen the menu!

Doing It Scared: when the only way out is through

Lack of neutrality affects more than topics. It can easily bleed over to having strong effects on our emotions. I often tell people my "favorite" part of my autism is the ability to feel extremely passionate about the things and people I care about. What I discuss less often is that my over-the-top feelings also create many of my major challenges. I feel strongly about almost everything. I love and I hate … without much time spent in the middle. I find this true of most people on the spectrum.

Some of us may learn to mask how we feel in an attempt not to look weird to other people. *Masking* is a term that's commonly used to describe what autistic people do to hide what feels normal to them for the benefit of other people. That might hide the emotional intensity, but it surely doesn't take the big feelings away. Emotional self-control is one of those rather abstract skills most people struggle with at some point. Those who experience emotions intensely and passionately (hint: autistic people) will often have very magnified struggles.

Although some might argue that learning to regulate feelings is masking and represents a negative reaction to living with autism, I don't believe that is always the case. Sometimes learning emotional balance is extraordinarily helpful. In my case, it has been life-changing. As someone who struggles with reading fluency and not tripping over words when nervous, you might imagine—correctly—I'd be apprehensive about either reading (especially aloud) or speaking to a group. But whether motivated by a Fear of Missing Out or a greater desire to share my story with the world, I came to control that apprehension so that it would not paralyze me. I learned if I let every big feeling get in my way, I'd get nothing done! Partly as a result, I've built strength for thriving under pressure. Not all types of pressure, and not all the time, but in scenarios like doing a keynote address, I stay seriously, incredibly, intensely nervous until I actually get started.

You have to understand that managing to get it done does *not* mean basic performance terror goes away. I just do it scared. I didn't learn overnight; it's taken years. My experience can parallel whatever brings out strong emotions in other autistic people. Can they learn to cope? To manage despite the big feelings? Yes, to varying degrees, they probably can. But they will benefit from supportive understanding of those all-or-nothing emotions so common in autistic people.

Avoiding Eye Contact: why it's hard and how to cope

My long-suffering mom tried for a long time to get me to practice eye contact. Over and over we'd role play the process of meeting a new person. What should I do? Where would I look? I never had any trouble with the practice sessions, since those were—of course—with my mom! Except none of it carried over when I was out in the wild of the general public. Meeting an actual, true new person? Having to talk to a "someone" for the first time—anyone from a checkout worker to a new student at school? Nope. Eye contact was not happening. I mostly couldn't handle it, practice or no practice. It simply was not the same thing with a stranger.

I've improved a little in adulthood, though some people would probably argue that point! But as an advocate for autistic people, I often field questions about *why* so many autistic people struggle with eye contact. The shortest answer I can give is that it feels physically uncomfortable. Autistic people describe eye contact as difficult because it can be stressful and distracting as they have to spend a great deal of mental energy on maintaining eye contact instead of focusing on the words. You might hear someone say that they can listen to you better if they're not actually looking at you. If they're looking somewhere other than at your eyes, they can focus better on your words. Eye contact with people I know well is not difficult. But eye contact with strangers or even new acquaintances feels too intimate. I find it very uncomfortable because I don't know them.

In many cultures neurotypical people associate eye contact with respect and active listening. So if you're avoiding eye contact, others assume you're disinterested or disrespectful. It might help to consider that an autistic person might be giving you *more* respect by declining eye contact than by maintaining it. If they want to focus entirely on what you're saying, they might need to look somewhere other than your eyes. For autistic people: if this is true for you, maybe you can try saying "I'm focusing hard on your words. That's easier for me to do if I'm not looking at you."

When parents are trying to build communication with young children, it may be helpful to teach them a vocal or physical sign that they're listening to you. If it's uncomfortable to the point of impossibility for a child to hold eye contact, perhaps they can learn to turn toward you or give some physical or vocal indication of attention. Body orientation alone can help a lot. "You don't have to look at my eyes, but at least turn toward me."

In working with my older learners, we have a discussion to make sure they know it is often a social expectation. I think I owe them that explanation, along with the following potential work-arounds:

- stating the reason for eye contact differences in a casual way,

- looking at some other aspect of the face, or

- body orientation.

The expectation for eye contact increases with age and maturity, so it's easy for this expectation to cross into masking, as already mentioned and which we'll discuss more later in Chapter 13. I believe it can be empowering to teach autistic people how to explain and/or compensate for lack of eye contact if they choose to do so. One tactic I use is to look at a different facial feature than the eyes. We might focus on the nose, the mouth, or the hair. The speaker might think we're a little shifty, but most likely they'll at least think we're listening!

Part 4: Interactions

I just found out I've been lonely for over a decade. I know what you're thinking. That's like saying I just found out I peed my pants ... how could I not feel it? Trust me, I felt it. Except even feeling it, I seem to keep finding excuses for why I haven't changed clothes yet. Every time I reach some new life milestone, I tell myself the next one will address that puddle of loneliness on the floor. I think I've been coercing myself into believing that lie since third grade.

Recently, while discovering what could be considered old journal entries on *my* computer, under *my* name ... I realized that *someone* has been recounting their experiences with loneliness. This mysterious activity seems to have been going on for a bunch of consecutive years. I recognized the characters immediately but, for some reason, the stories themselves felt cold, wet, and unfamiliar. Maybe they didn't feel like *my* stories, because I've been telling myself for a very long time that those are just chapters.

At this point in my life, I've grown increasingly intolerant of that unpleasant sensation that's all about being on the outside looking in. When I'm around others and have any reason at all to think they don't want me there or need me there, my awareness of that cold, wet feeling sharply increases. The truth about loneliness? I'm still worried that while new chapters are being written, the storyline itself won't have the dramatic change I've been imagining.

Chapter 12

Loneliness: Isolation and Its Fallout

Unfortunately, my outsider situation is incredibly common. What's far less common is recognizing the problem as one needing assistance. Somehow we have to get past the idea that loneliness—lack of social connection—is a problem separate from other behavioral/educational issues. It's not only *just* as important, but it might also be *more* important.

Critical Connections: a human necessity

Human beings have to have connections! We need connection with other humans just like we need food, water, and shelter. We can't function without attention from and camaraderie with other people. Human nature *demands* access to a supportive group of other humans. However, exactly for that same reason—because we've been wired to survive together, cooperatively—our behavior always has to align with the common interest of the group. Unfortunately, autistic individuals' communication and social skill deficits can cause disruptive or dangerous behaviors. Frequent crying spells, swatting at others, cursing, or defecating on the floor of a classroom won't build anyone's social connection. Obviously, such behaviors will cause social isolation, making it non-optional to find ways to help them make necessary changes.

Seeking attention or connection inappropriately can have dire consequences, including social isolation and eventual cognitive decline. If the decline is severe enough, even the most resilient person might eventually hit life's unsubscribe button. A recent study revealed that suicide mortality among autistic adults is nine times more common than among the general population (Hirvikoski and Blomqvist 2015). In less extreme circumstances, loneliness, which therapists consider the diet version of social isolation, is linked to shorter life spans.

That loneliness? For me, the hardest part of being autistic has been the loneliness that comes with it. I was always a loner, but never by choice. I know others on the spectrum experience this as well. Although most autistic adults experience chronic loneliness, I don't think it has to be that way. With the rise in social acceptance and increased knowledge on how to best teach autistic people, autism shouldn't have to mean a person will be lonely. What if we could shift away from focusing on social connection as a *separate* goal and, instead, focus more on social connection as the very basis for removing barriers and building skills? If we could, I believe all the efforts to increase quality of life for autistic people would get an immediate, powerful boost!

Here's an example of a common situation. A 10-year-old with significant expressive language delays struggles to maintain meaningful relationships with his classmates. He speaks in short sentences and is able to read, write, and do math at a third-grade level. As a result of his language deficits, he has a specialized classroom placement. Based on his assessment, the report noted that he could not understand traditional figures of speech ("raining cats and dogs") or identify community helpers (police officer or firefighter). He frequently approaches his peers and squeals excitedly in their faces and then initiates a string of words from his favorite character, Percy, from *Thomas & Friends*. Although it may be more straightforward for his support staff to focus on catching him up on the gaps found in his language assessment, if he doesn't know how to engage with his classmates, we need to prioritize building social connections, which will have a far bigger impact on his life.

Awareness Versus Acceptance: both matter

What does springtime mean to me? The beginning of the annual great debate about Autism Awareness versus Autism Acceptance. Each year people spend far too much time questioning word choices so that we will celebrate the "correct" thing in April. A question that often shows up in comments on my social media platforms is "What's the difference between autism awareness and autism acceptance?" A common quote works: "If you are aware, you know who I am; if you are accepting, you are happy to see me." If you're aware, then you know what autism is and how it affects everyone differently. Acceptance means you don't exclude or discount me because I'm different.

As to the ongoing battle in the autism community about whether awareness or acceptance is more important, I don't think the answer is as simple as a single word choice. I think each person, and therefore each community, is different. While some argue that we have already achieved worldwide awareness, there are certainly places that lack diagnostic options at all. In those locations, becoming aware would be a good place to start. There are other places in the world that have a fair amount of awareness about autism, but some improvement on the acceptance part would, indeed, be a happy thing. Even when there is awareness, it is often limited to a knowledge of a small sliver of the spectrum. I am constantly frustrated by people's beliefs that they have already checked the autism awareness box because they've heard the word and they know a single autistic person. I really hope that people will dig deeper before congratulating themselves on their awareness. And, of course, acceptance takes even more work.

Self-acceptance factors here as well. Understanding and loving oneself can be essential for success in adulthood. Knowledge and acceptance by family members can make a world of difference for a child. Back in the beginning, I described the lag in my autism diagnosis. As said before, I'm thankful my mom pursued a diagnosis, even when some professionals brushed off her concerns. In my distorted self-perception before diagnosis, I believed completely that I wasn't human. I thought I belonged to another species but just looked human. My view of myself was extremely negative. I believed I was unintelligent and "bad." A diagnosis can give access to support that wouldn't be there otherwise. A diagnosis also gave me an accurate basis to correct that problematic self-image. A formal diagnosis that I can share with others if I choose helps prevent the world from calling me something much worse than autistic, and, *yes*, that happened to me many times prior to knowing what to call my challenges.

For me, I learned about my academic challenges first, as a follow-up to the report my mom received when I was 10. I remember confessing to my sleepover friend at the time that I had dyslexia, thinking that it explained all my quirks. It wasn't until I was a young teen that I got a better understanding of the complexities of being me. Around the time I entered Project Hope Foundation's school program, I heard the word *Asperger's* and then my mom sat me down to look at a message board (which functioned like an old-school Reddit) called Wrong Planet. It was truly transformative for me to see that I was not alone in my thought processes, which made sense to me but not to others. People there understood why I spent a year introducing myself as a K-9 (because my name started with K and I was then nine years old.) From there, we watched a movie about Temple Grandin. While I didn't necessarily identify with her childhood challenges, I related to her issues of resistance to change and focused passionate interests.

I am a strong believer in making sure that children know about their diagnosis as soon as it makes sense for them. If you don't give them the words, they will come up with their own. *Autistic* is a much better term than *weird* and *stupid*.

Self-acceptance matters probably more than any other factor. Yet general acceptance from friends and non-family is a close runner-up. If you're a neurotypical person reading for perspective, have you ever thought about why deliberately adding an autistic friend to your social circle would be a life-enriching upgrade? Here are a few factors you might not have yet considered.

- **Capacity for thoughtfulness.** We have strong preferences and opinions. Once we understand what *your* strong preferences are, we can recognize the significance of what's important to you.

- **Acceptance of others.** Many of us do not dilute our own personalities, meaning we can feel appreciation for the person you really are, rather than who others might expect you to be.

- **Unique ways of showing love.** Whether we give you a cool rock we found or write a thoughtful note, most of us have ways to show we care that might be different and richer than what you're used to.

For us autistic people, finding a group with similar interests is a great starting point. One positive autism trait can be our ability to feel passionate about and be extremely knowledgeable on certain topics. Capitalizing on that trait is one really helpful way for us to build connections with others. If taking part in small talk and chit-chat about the weather is challenging or just plain boring, we might have better success trying to connect with others who have similar interests.

I will caution that the phrase *sharing interests* is broad and may need some nuanced practice. This is true about my own passionate interest in dogs. My canine companions are a huge interest for me, but, statistically speaking, if you like dogs, you might not like them the right way for me … which is, of course, *my* way! You may be the kind of dog-lover who considers your pet to be a fur baby. I am anti-anthropomorphism. I want my dogs to be dogs, and we will probably never agree on that aspect!

Friendships: intentional teaching of skills

Once when I was very little, I messed up what could have been a perfectly fun sleepover with friends by roaring at them and trying to chase them around the house with my best imitation from my favorite movie, *The Lion King*. My friends probably also liked that movie. But they sure didn't like my method of trying to talk about it. In other words, they didn't like it the right way. My mom's memories of the situation are more stark than my own. I had enormous trouble starting the most basic of conversations with peers. Sure, I had conversational opportunities, and I desperately wanted to engage. But I didn't always have the skills to take correct advantage. I couldn't capitalize appropriately on a chance when it came my way. Knowing when, where, and with whom something is socially appropriate to discuss has limited value without enough understanding of how—literally *how*—to discuss it. (Word to the wise ... roaring and chasing do not work). Even recognizing a common interest with another person doesn't do you much good if you don't know what words to use to talk about that interest—or when to stop. So how do you fix that?

One summer I worked with a nine-year-old autistic girl who was really interested in dolls. She, like me as a child, also desperately wanted to play with another little girl in our therapy clinic. She would bring the dolls to show the other girl, but beyond simply looking at the dolls together, the encounter had nowhere else to go and would fizzle out within minutes ... every single time. Of course this left my young client feeling very sad. Based on observing her obvious interest in playing dolls with the other girl, the two of us generated a plan to meet her goal of playing dolls, which involved step-by-step instructions.

- We started by naming the dolls.

- Next we practiced some actions to do with the dolls. I showed how we could hold, feed, and push the dolls on a swing.

- From there, I taught her some language to go along with the activity. "She needs to eat!" "I'm going to give her a big push."

Socially or clinically, at home or at school, people find fulfillment when they achieve goals that allow them to take advantage of their opportunities!

Professionals and educators—and, yes, even parents—often create goals for autistic people based on where they perceive the person is "behind." Assessments have value, but they also have limits. It's important to acknowledge and remember they are not all-encompassing. With the child and the dolls, I observed where my client's natural motivation carried her. From there, I could decipher which things *she* would find value in learning. I find that most often people *want* to learn what allows them to *access* their opportunities.

Hidden Requests: missing the meaning

If you're trying to build a relationship with an autistic person, I want to help you notice a phenomenon that is often a barrier for us. Once you recognize it, you will see it happening in nearly every social exchange. People do this thing all the time and they don't even realize it. I'm talking about hidden requests, which are attempts to get something without ever actually asking for it. If you're autistic, that can be a problem because our brains have to make a conscious effort to infer the additional information behind the words. As we discussed earlier, we thrive with directness. Here are some examples.

- **Hidden Request Statement**: "Ooooh! Those cookies look delicious!"
  Direct Translation: "Is it okay for me to have a cookie?"

- **Hidden Request Statement**: "This looks really hard. It would be great to get some assistance."
  Direct Translation: "Can you help me? I'm feeling overwhelmed."

- **Hidden Request Statement**: "I was thinking about having some friends over on Saturday night."
  Direct Translation: "Would you mind if I had people over?"

- **Hidden Request Statement**: "I keep seeing excellent reviews for that new Chinese restaurant down the street."
  Direct Translation: "Are you interested in trying that new Chinese restaurant with me?"

Calling it a hidden request sounds malicious, but that's *not* usually the case. In fact, most of the time, the intention is to be polite. This type of indirect communication is often less of an autistic versus neurotypical issue, and more of a cultural thing. For example, German culture is often considered as being direct, while southern United States culture is known for burying meanings in indirectness. Culture aside, most people tend to be more indirect with people they just met and more direct with those they know well.

It just so happens that many (but not all) autistic people need a more direct approach, which can be more or less challenging depending on the culture they grew up with. Learning about different communication styles gives everyone (neurodivergent *and* neurotypical) a chance to better understand each other.

Some of my autistic followers take a different approach. They have declared that they choose to "advocate" by refusing to acknowledge hidden requests because it is indirect communication that doesn't meet their needs. Maybe because I enjoy a debate, I have questioned that stance. To me, if you prefer direct communication, you must yourself be direct! I think it is better to flat-out say, "I do best with direct communication. If you'd like me to do something for you, you'll have to ask me directly." Because refusing to acknowledge people who communicate indirectly *is* in itself indirect. So if you value direct communication in the way that I do, why not just tell people that instead of ignoring them? Of course, this all assumes that the person in question has the communication skills to advocate for themselves, which is not the case for everyone on the spectrum.

You may be wondering whether the use of direct questions conflicts with my early advice about offering "candy bowls" of declarative statements instead of questions. My candy-bowl advice relates to helping build conversation without imposing demands for a response. This section refers to asking direct questions rather than embedding hidden demands in statements.

Distinguishing Empathy: not understanding doesn't mean not caring

I'd ruined a library book, and I was crying hysterically. What bothered me wasn't about the book. In fact, in my five-year-old mind, I was pretty sure I'd improved the book. What upset me so much was having disappointed the librarian, causing her look of distress. I couldn't read yet, but I could understand the book Mom had read to me just fine, and so far as I was concerned, the illustrations in the little book simply did not match the details I was hearing. So I fixed them. Extensively. In detail. On every page.

and as he settled on a branch, he watched peacefully the sun sink below the horizon.

16

Chapter 3

17

Mom promptly marched me back to the library to confess my sins. I was completely unrepentant, but I saw the librarian's face change expression, and—no matter how right I thought I was—it was obvious to my young self I'd made her sad. I didn't have a sophisticated enough understanding of human emotion to define all the details, but I could tell she was unhappy, and I had caused it! Which made *me* very, very unhappy! Far too often others think autistic people don't feel empathy, but that's really far from the truth, at least for some of us. We might struggle to *understand* another's emotion, but we don't struggle to feel empathetic about what we *do* understand. Autistic people usually feel everything larger than average. On that long-ago day, even while I was still trying to explain to the librarian why the book was so much better with my editing, it was the look on her face that did me in. Cue a full-scale sobbing fit it took my mom hours to resolve.

At a recent conference the host asked me to choose one topic I thought was a common, problematic misconception, so I chose this exact area: neurotypical people often think autistic people don't care about others' feelings. Autistic people *do* experience empathy. Very often we experience it at levels far above normal, just like we feel almost everything else—good or bad—at levels above normal. This is, for example, a big part of why travel can be a huge challenge for me. When I'm in a big city, that's new to me, and I encounter unhoused people living on the street, that's something I almost can't get past well enough to manage my speaking engagement.

For many autistic people, the major challenge in this area is identifying what someone else feels when it's different from what we feel. But *not understanding* someone's perspective and *not caring* about someone's perspective are totally different. I can't speak for all autistic people, but I believe most of us *do* care about others' feelings. Identifying others' feelings will play a role, but we also might not understand how to respond.

Circling back to our discussion on direct communication, many times it would be extremely helpful to us if you neurotypical people would simply say what you want or need to help us respond in the best way to demonstrate our care for you.

- "If I'm crying, I'd like for you to ask me what's wrong so I know it's okay to tell you."

- "If I'm sitting with my head down, leave me alone for a little while so I can recuperate."

- Fill in your own blank with "When I do [X], please do [Y]."

It's fair to say autism has the same cross-section of responses as all of humanity—maybe some *don't* care, just like some neurotypical people don't care. Beyond that, some on the spectrum haven't yet gained the skills to help them tap into responses which will be meaningful to you. But please don't assume we're never going to care *because* we're autistic. It's possible that all we need to know is what's best to do.

Chapter 13

Flying Dolphins: Sorting Out Social Complications

A few years ago, a co-worker was fired because of me. Yes, really. Both of us were providing therapy sessions in a shared room, and, for reasons I didn't understand, my co-worker asked if I'd like to try her home-made sauce. When I politely declined, she relentlessly pressed the issue. This co-worker knew about my autism diagnosis and began attempting to turn the exchange into a big joke about my lack of flexibility. I still didn't want her sauce, and besides, we were supposed to be providing therapy, not running taste tests on each other's lunches. But she wouldn't give up. She started following me around the room waving a sample on her finger. Despite my attempts to avoid her, she eventually cornered me and actually stuck her sauce-laden finger into my mouth. Yuck!

Pretty inappropriate, right? But you know what's probably the most bizarre part? I just didn't get it! I thought this was a normal way for co-workers to joke around, and I tried very hard to be a good sport. It wasn't until at least a week later when I relayed this episode to my supervisor—me, still trying to see it as a joke—that I learned all the reasons it was definitely no laughing matter. End-game? Sauce-finger was fired. I found myself on the receiving end of some rather intense explanations about unacceptable behavior and the need to speak up.

So, my point … what's a person with that little understanding of social norms doing trying to advise *you* about interactions? Well, you might be surprised. I've learned a lot since then, and I might be better at teaching those interactions than you think. And there are specific reasons for that.

Eagles & Dolphins: innate versus learned skills

Saying some autistic people are good at teaching social skills might sound a little like saying some dolphins make good flight instructors. Despite their inherent navigation skills, dolphins aren't even remotely familiar with the concepts of aerodynamics, flight planning, or aviation safety. The crucial components of being a pilot are completely foreign to them. But in the imaginary world of analogies, what if there were a handful of dolphins who had an interest in all things aviation? Well, through dedication and hard work, perhaps a few could obtain a commercial pilot's license. If that happened, and if you ever asked a dolphin pilot to teach you about aviation, the dolphin could back up flight knowledge with personal experience, because they remember with great intensity what it was like to learn that information!

By contrast, if you asked an eagle about aviation, they'd more likely just stare at you blankly. And no, not because eagles don't talk. This is an analogy, remember? Everything talks! Eagles begin to fly by 14 weeks. Aside from some general pointers, an eagle probably can't mentally deconstruct *how* to fly, because they've never had to construct it in the first place. They have little or no memory of not knowing how.

In this analogy, I'm the dolphin who had to put years of practice into learning something that does *not* come naturally. As an autistic person, you can wander around your world, making decisions, trying to do your thing, and no one gives you *any* instructions on how to do life without making people mad! Nobody tells you how to express a spicy opinion. Or how to tell someone their idea is the equivalent of hot-dog water. Or how to navigate conflict involving multiple people. So you make your best attempt with no directions and maybe you get it right. Of course, no one tells you if you get it right. So if you did, you'll never know why or how to do it again. And what really sucks? By contrast you will *always* find out if you did it wrong! People get upset with you, yet about half the time they, themselves, can't articulate a reasonable alternative action. But they still expect you to get better—so long as you *don't* do whatever it was you just did.

All that confusion is something I've had to learn to sort through by deliberate focus, careful attention, and a whole lot of questions asked of people I trust. Not only did I have to *learn* step by step, but I have to *think* about it that same way—step by step—every day of my life. For me, it's not an automatic process, but an endless series of conscious choices I must forever keep in mind. Since I'm intimately familiar with the process, and also because it's a constant challenge in my life, it's pretty easy for me (the dolphin aviator) to teach those social skills to other autistic people. As soaring eagles, neurotypical therapists have such a strong familiarity with social skills that it can get in the way of teaching. Those skills come so naturally that they have difficulty deconstructing and explaining the pieces.

What you need to carry away from the idea of dolphin pilots is a real understanding that in almost any social setting, relationships with autistic people will differ from relationships with neurotypical people. A primary reason is the matter of social norms, those unwritten rules that autistic people struggle to understand. In fact, it's more than struggling to understand. It starts with recognizing that such unwritten rules even exist. It's more like that dolphin in the analogy realizing, "Wait! You mean flight is possible and I could learn?"

Navigating Society: some social skills hacks

To my non-autistic readers who have never been on the receiving end of a correction for *not* playing along and are wondering, "Is she making a bigger deal of this than it actually is?" Well, let's be blunt. No! Autistic people struggle with this almost constantly, whether in private or professional settings. Even if you scheduled a meeting to discuss a project with someone, most of society considers it rude to begin discussing said project before you give a few exchanges of "How are you/ How was your weekend/ Nice weather we're having, huh?" It's a constant challenge for me!

Allow me to elaborate with a few of the strategies I had to learn in order to navigate society as a flying dolphin.

- Offering a greeting before doing anything else appears to be a requirement, and I have learned that the greeting is valid only if it comes with a friendly face. Speaking from experience, "Hi," muttered under your breath, accompanied by fleeting eye contact and a grimace that suggests somebody peed in your corn flakes this morning, does *not* count. While we're on the subject, it's also worth noting that "Mmhmm" is not considered a valid response to the greeting, "Good morning."

- Small talk makes no sense to me and is, in fact, quite annoying. But it seems to be essential, so I have come up with a great social hack for the requisite small talk before initiating a real conversation. Just refer to the day of the week. I've never understood why people love this, but they sure do.

  - "It's Monday!" or "It's Friday!" seems to do the trick when you don't know what else to use. People almost always respond favorably, "It sure is!" or "Thank goodness!"

  - In fact, the opposite can also be just as effective. Amazingly, "It's not Monday!" or "It's not Friday!" also elicits positive feedback: "You're so right!"

- A positive attitude is expected when speaking to acquaintances, co-workers, neighbors, and some community helpers. Note that the positivity mandate seems to include almost everything!

    o "How are the kids doing?" Unless the kids have passed away or are newly ill, the right answer is, "The kids are great!"

    o "How are things at work going?" Unless your work place was just involved in a recent scandal, you should say, "Things are busy, but good!"

- Many questions do not require honest answers. In fact, honesty is discouraged. Basically, we're all just following a script, which is pretty obvious in scenarios like this one. Someone asks you, "What did you get up to last weekend?" Unless you found the cure to cancer or were diagnosed with cancer, your response should be something like: "We just hung out and relaxed."

- Make your criticism soft. This one is tricky because while it's incredibly hard to give constructive criticism in a tactful way, it's almost always unfair to expect the person on the receiving end just to accept criticism regardless of how it's dished out. Even if they've just done something dumb, stupid, or wrong, no one likes to hear that. If the goal is for them to improve, acknowledging that the thing was dumb, stupid, or wrong won't help them move closer to the desired outcome. A common way to soften this kind of feedback is to use "I" statements. These are focused on you and your perspective rather than the other person's mistakes.

    o "Next time, I would...."

    o "When this happens to me, I usually...."

    o "What has worked for me in the past...."

- Respond to people's statements before making your own. This one is not as difficult as softening criticism, but, unfortunately, people have differing opinions on what the right way to do this looks like. For example, if I've just shared a story about going to the dentist to get a cavity filled, some people may be inclined to respond by sharing a time they went to the dentist. Others would say it's polite to first give some sort of acknowledgement response before launching into your story, even if it's still related to the same topic. While many in the neurodivergent community use their own related stories to show empathy and compassion, not everyone will see it that way. Because everyone seems to have a different perspective on this, I've learned to just default to saying something that provides recognition to what's just been said before sharing something related to myself. Even something as simple as "Wow, that does sound difficult!" or "I can't believe that happened to you."

Hidden Rules: "universal" knowledge isn't so universal

Even for language-abled people like myself, navigating social exchanges can be extremely difficult and exhausting. Our world is full of such challenges, and we are forever finding out about new ones. That invisible trip-wire is always waiting for us. The older we grow and the more social experience we have, the more we learn to be wary, but wariness alone won't solve the problem. The largest complication for us remains others' assumptions that we have a certain amount of pre-existing knowledge. This isn't knowledge anyone is going to give us explicitly; we're just expected to know.

Want examples? Here's one: this magical "universal" knowledge people are just expected to have about knowing when in a conversation it's their turn to speak. Most people don't learn conversational turn-taking in a formal way. In fact, if you asked your Friendly Neighborhood Non-Autistic Person to describe that process, they probably couldn't articulate the rule or tell how to follow it properly. If I asked, "How do I know when I can talk and how long should I speak?" Your Friendly Neighborhood Non-Autistic Person will probably say something like: "When someone else talks, you wait for a little while, then you'll just know when it's your turn. And then after you've gone on for a little while, you'll get a sense of when to stop." Can you imagine if we taught driver's ed like that? Crazy! But that's how many would attempt to explain the process and believe that they had done so with specificity.

Hidden rules are best understood as cultural rules (often connected to overarching values) that we're all just expected to both understand and follow with no formalized instruction. If a mysterious, hidden rule is broken, often a lot of eye rolling happens or you—the rule breaker—find people avoiding you from embarrassment or frustration with your behavior. The French language has a great term for this concept: *faux pas.* Literally a "false step," a "people oops."

Most Friendly Neighborhood Non-Autistic People have a default setting of seeing a minor *faux pas.* When that happens they typically recognize the "oops" immediately after the infraction. Many autistic people don't get the "oops" sensation after a *faux pas* and have no recognition that a mistake happened. Others of us see the aftermath. We may see the eye rolls. We may notice people drifting away or avoiding us altogether. But we usually do not know why—because no one has ever taught us the rule!

Many social skills do *not* come to us naturally, so it's safe to assume we've fought long and hard for the ones we do have. Far too often neurotypical people chalk up our "oops" mistakes as willful errors because of their underlying assumption that everyone has a certain amount of existing knowledge. They totally fail to recognize the autistic person has never had any idea of that social construct. To me, this is a failure of perception—one of those challenges usually attributed to those of us with autism! It's an excellent chance to understand how *we* feel so much of the time. In these situations, you might think, "Well, how was I supposed to know she didn't know?" I say, "Thank you. That's exactly my point. *That's* how it works for us!"

If you have any thought that this assumption of knowledge issue might be at all unusual, let me assure you it's an everyday problem for us. It's close to an every-conversation, every-encounter problem. How can the rest of the world help us?

- Challenge your inner assumption that "everybody knows that!" Please understand that autistic people very likely do not know that.

- Remember the section on direct communication. Fill in the gaps by helping us understand what to do. This may require you to restate information more clearly or give us specific guidance.

- Many families and caretakers of people with profound autism are likely to find themselves trying to cushion experiences with others, constantly scanning, on-guard, looking for factors the autistic person appears to be ignoring. They will be the ones facilitating interaction … endlessly smiling, explaining, and educating to help foster community understanding and support. Respond with kindness.

Many of the most common social interaction issues between autistic and neurotypical people can be re-framed and better understood by remembering that one analogy: a world full of eagles is trying to build relationships with a bunch of dolphins who are still learning the many rules of aerial navigation.

Masking: a closer look

If I'm trying to convince someone I am *not* upset, but I'm talking to them while sitting on the floor with my head hidden under a blanket … I'm probably not doing a great job conveying "not upset." If this seems obvious to you, please know that, for me, understanding this little fact was a moment of significant personal growth. It might have been the most significant in a long string of events through which I decided masking pretty much never works for me, even despite repeated thoughts like, "Surely giving them *this* behavior will work *this* time!" (It didn't.) What's masking, and why did my blanket-covered moment of clarity matter so much?

Masking is a hot topic in the social media world, but it needs a bit more nuanced discussion than is possible in a TikTok video.

Masking our true selves, repressing our behavior and/or adding non-authentic behavior to show everyone how normal we are, can become acutely harmful. We can inhibit ourselves to the point of losing personality in favor of shallow social acceptance. We may squelch the traits that make us uniquely ourselves. You'll never get to experience my passionate love of rollercoasters if I suppress my enthusiasm so that I don't stand out.

Additionally, it requires a ridiculous amount of effort, often draining us of our ability to do anything else but focus on maintaining the mask. We give up substance for surface level interaction. I can't focus on following a complex conversation if I am using all my energy on monitoring my eye contact.

And, at least in my case, masking is not even very effective. My autism is very much me ... and it simply shows up in ways that I don't ever consciously realize. I am always a little surprised when I catch glimpses of myself in random video clips. I could have sworn that I am walking around looking exactly like everyone else—it doesn't register with me until I see that I unconsciously keep my hands in T-Rex position!

I'll give you another example from my life. My unfiltered directness often comes across as being witty, which lots of people see as charming or humorous. When I get into an argument, my wittiness tags along. Unfortunately, in an argument wit can often sound rude or snarky. I spent most of my teenage years trying to balance out this part of myself, usually at my mother's expense. As an adult, with more on the line than losing my phone privileges for being disrespectful, I'm still trying to find that balance. Within an argument, I can spend 100% of my focus making sure both my words and my tone sound polite, but this leaves zero percent of my brain left to regulate my facial expression or body language. I often walk away from conflict scenarios thinking that other people couldn't tell that I was upset because I was so polite and respectful when I spoke. But as events turn out, guess what? Other people can both hear *and* see me! Adjusting my words and tone isn't always going to be enough, and I can create more trouble than I solve … sitting there with that blanket over my head, counting on my words to convince everyone into believing I'm just fine.

Now, with all that said, remember that I'm also a therapist. Do I teach my autistic clients to mask? The short answer is no, not in the sense of encouraging them continually or constantly to repress their natural personality. But adjusting your behavior to fit a situation is a skill all humans should be aware of and then have the *choice* to use or not. If you don't know it exists, you can't make the choice.

Whether or not we realize it, all humans mask! That's to say that most people change their behavior based on who we're with and where we are. Usually, you show your best friend, your boss, your mother, and your children different versions of yourself. A good communicator can change their words, style of speaking, body language, and behavior based on who they're with and what their goals are.

So as a therapist, I do my best to teach clients what this concept is, why it can be helpful, and how people do it. Here's why that's both ethical and important: people need to understand the concept to empower them to choose *how*—or even *if*—they do something with it. It would be unethical for me to withhold this important fact about human behavior, considering that most neurotypical people are already conceptually aware of it and probably using it to some extent. In fact, to me, if I have information and choose to withhold it from them, I am being unkind—perhaps even cruel.

For example, I work with an 18-year-old language-abled young man who has expressed great interest in building relationships with his neurotypical youth group at church. One of his stims is to pace in circles waving his arms around. Because he didn't make any noise while doing so, he thought people wouldn't pay attention. He's a tall guy and his gestures are big, so I knew that the group of non-autistic people certainly *would* notice. Consequently, I felt I needed to make sure he understood the group's possible responses. I added that he certainly could continue to do so. He could explain to his peers why he engaged in that particular behavior, or he could simply let them react to him in whatever way happened. He could implement other behaviors that might provide the same sensory input. My goal was not to encourage him to suppress his authentic self, but to provide him with direct information so that he could make informed choices. He could then choose to use that information—or not—in pursuing his goal of finding a girlfriend within that group.

So, let's recap: do I teach my clients to mask their autism? No. I teach them concepts related to interacting with different audiences to give them more choices about the types of people they want to engage with and how to do so.

Chapter 14

Building Independence

I almost lost my driver's license at the ripe age of 20. People don't always believe me when I tell that tale, which grew out of my first experience with a speeding ticket. I didn't know when and how to pay the fee and ultimately had to leave work abruptly for court (thank you, Poor Time Management). When I arrived, I sassed the judge when she asked if I understood the consequences of not paying a ticket. In response, she increased my fee and gave me points on my license. It was a series of unnecessary, unfortunate events.

This entire episode happened because of my inability to manage time, prioritize, and plan for the future. Beyond that, my heightened emotional state made me less able to inhibit my snarky remarks. As with so many aspects of life, all people can, and do, experience these things at some point. However, at the risk of too much repetition, understanding autism means remembering that many such problems are ones of scale. Any given skill might take longer for an autistic person to learn, be harder to learn, and require continued practice until much later in life than what's expected for neurotypical people.

Executive Function: harder than it looks

A classic example of this kind of delayed learning and increased challenge applies to the term *executive functioning*. Executive functioning has become an often-used term referring to the ability to plan, monitor, and successfully execute goals. It includes what you pay attention to, your working memory, your inhibitions, and problem-solving.

When people talk about *adulting,* they're usually referring to this skill set we call executive functioning. They mean the part of the human brain that can make good choices about activities and priorities. Such skills typically begin developing around age three and continue until early adulthood, but people with a variety of neurological differences have significant, measurable deficits in this area. I'm here to tell you that the struggles are real for those of us who are autistic, even when your child, friend, or client seems to have a great number of skills.

For me, one area where the challenges come into play is with working memory. Executive functioning relies on working memory (the brain's version of a sticky note), which allows us to hold new information in place so the brain can connect it to existing information. When we have trouble with working memory, difficulties arise in following multi-step instructions, organizing our thoughts, and converting information into long-term memory.

Newly acquired, important information seems to float around aimlessly in my brain for a couple of hours, never finding a place to land. The task in front of me seems to laugh as I frantically search my brain for information I just had! Once I finally locate and grab the information, I begrudgingly drag it back to the task, only to find that the original task has now floated away as well. Working memory deficits can affect our ability to read, learn new things, and make decisions. Each of those functions requires us to hold on to information briefly in order to categorize it for long-term storage.

I try to accommodate for my memory issues by writing as many notes as I possibly can, but I've yet to find a solution for what to do when you read the note and still can't remember what to do with the information. If any of this sounds familiar to you, you are not alone, and you (or your children) are not stupid! And it sometimes explains the inability to make good decisions … oh, you know … like showing up in court when you're supposed to.

Decisions: relying on visuals

To protect my driver's license, my sanity, and other commodities I consider important, I now live my life based on a whiteboard with clearly separated sections. I can consult appropriate lists for everything from What I Need to Buy, Tasks to Do, What I Need Help With, and more. Not everyone will thrive on this system, but I do. Especially when autism happens along with a learning disability—or more than one, like mine—visual representation may prove to be your friend.

While I'm not about to tell you my system will work for everyone, I want to get you thinking about external options to help someone know and remember all the available choices. Most decisions require a person to store and organize information and then, ultimately, take action. The more information involved, the harder the task. Because this process can be difficult for people on the spectrum, it often leaves us in a state of "decision paralysis." This will look different for each individual depending on their other skills, but I rely on my whiteboard, and maybe the autistic person in your life needs something similar. If your brain can't process all that information internally, you need to do it externally.

Some people cannot make a choice without having a visual display of options, a *choice board!* Some people manage this task better when they can see every option. Others find that overwhelming and do best when faced with only two to four options. The number of choices involved must be assessed case by case, but having options presented in one place helps us organize our thoughts and take action. Make it as simple or as complex as needed.

When working with children, I often use a choice board for play activities. It might have pictures. Or just words. It might have moveable parts for reorganization or inclusion of different options at different times. But it would include choices appropriate for that client:

- walk,

- color,

- iPad,

- gym,

- swing,

- puzzle,

- book,

- game, and/or

- snack.

As I noted earlier, we often can't make a choice until we have seen the menu!

Goals: the collaboration approach

A natural off-shoot from decision making is goal setting. In the best of all worlds, we all reach the point of setting goals for ourselves. However, in the real world, people often lack enough self-awareness to choose goals that will serve their desires. If you are in the position of helping someone with that process, I think it is critical to tie those goals to something of ultimate value to that individual. Lectures or accusatory statements do not serve your purpose. That's true even when talking to yourself about your own goals. Instead, the therapist/teacher/parent needs to act as a second person on the same team, working towards a common goal.

I had a student who used to scream at his peers when they didn't immediately respond to his requests. My goal was to teach him skills to gain attention appropriately. To get him on board with this, I needed to tie *my* goal to an outcome that is important to *him*. So I approached him by saying "I noticed sometimes when we hang out with your friends, they don't always listen to you, and that seems to make you really upset."

He was more likely to agree with my assessment because I identified what he's seeking in that situation. I explained it can't be fun for him to need to yell at them, and even worse, that they still don't listen. At that point, I've (1) provided an empathy statement, (2) identified his intention, and (3) illustrated to him that his current process isn't providing the results he wants.

Then, I could propose my alternative: "I have an idea to help get them to listen to you." He became interested because I've just suggested I can fix this problem he obviously cares about. So we tried something as a suggestion: "When you say something and they don't answer, instead of yelling, stand up, go tap on their shoulder and say it again. That should make sure they answer. If they still don't, come tell me and I'll help you."

He might not have been motivated by following rules for gaining attention, being perceived as polite, or being the model of an inside voice. But I'd outlined my goal as a means for him to get what *he* wants.

Recapping: to develop meaningful goals in any process of goal-setting, it is important to identify a person's motivation to engage in a behavior. Remember that you don't always have to guess. If their language skills make it possible, you can just ask! It sounds so basic, but people often overlook the power of a direct question. An answer might surprise you when you ask,

> "What do you want right now?"

> **or**

> "When you [specify behavior], what do you want to happen?"

Whenever possible, I believe therapists and parents should set goals *with* people, not *for* them. Such a collaborative approach might require you to bring a problem to someone's attention first and then explain how you can help remove the barriers to solving the problem.

Of course, many on the spectrum are unable to answer those kinds of questions. For this segment of the autistic population, it is critical for us to use all their behavioral cues to make our best guess about their motivations and about the skills they need to achieve their objectives. If a person can't yet take part in setting goals, you'll have to observe their daily problems or frustrations to generate meaningful goals.

Accommodations: the world isn't designed for naked hiking

So what exactly is an *accommodation?* Let's start by debunking a common misconception. You've probably heard the description of an accommodation as a crutch. That erroneous analogy creates ongoing trouble for us who are coping with autism. Whether for yourself or for your child, it might help to plan in advance how to respond when you encounter someone who believes "using [something] as a crutch" means relying on a support that's not actually needed. To me, the assumption implies a person uses an accommodation as a lazy shortcut, and that certainly never made any sense to me. Consider crutches. In the literal sense, people use the medical device of a crutch when they have difficulty walking. Have you ever seen an able-bodied human using crutches to make walking easier? That's beyond ridiculous. Using crutches is harder than walking without them! Way harder. In reality, disability accommodations all carry that same logic. Accommodations are *not* the easy way out. In fact, acquiring and using a disability accommodation is often far more difficult than if it were possible just to go without.

It's a lot more work to purchase and/or train a service dog, to adjust to medications, or go through the trial-and-error of different therapies than it ever would be to simply not need such things at all. To avoid accommodations for fear they'd become a crutch sounds silly to me. No sane human uses crutches when the crutches aren't actually needed. Similarly, no one wants to bother with using proper disability accommodations longer than they need to.

It would help most neurotypical—and probably many autistic—people to spend a little more time considering the truth that accommodations do not make things easier. *They make things possible.* Accommodations restore access to an environment or activity. They're what, despite their inconvenience, restore options to a human with a disability.

Someone asked me recently, "If a disabled person did need something different, wouldn't it be considered a special need?" I thought that was a great question! I can only speak to this from my own experience, but I'd argue that the *need* itself isn't special. We all have the same basic human needs. It's not the needs that are different. The method of meeting the needs might look different, but the needs themselves are the same. It's a small shift, but our language really does matter. And this is one potential shift we can make that brings us (neurotypical and neurodivergent/disabled people) closer together. I like to look for ways that we're the same because we're better together.

Unfortunately, the world doesn't often keep people with disabilities in mind when designing processes. Many of us have to be innovative in generating solutions. Our practical limitations aren't what most people experience. Even fewer understand them. Because of this lack of understanding, some people believe that disability supports should happen only with the stipulation that they be faded or removed within a specified timeframe. For this flawed logic, here's one of my favorite disability accommodation analogies.

What if I told you that a disabled person going without a needed accommodation is like hiking in the nude? Explanations are in order. Hikers do certain things to support themselves so they can reach their goals: wearing hiking boots, carrying a backpack, and applying bug spray. Just because they have the hiking boots on does not mean the hike becomes easy. Having a backpack will not mean they're never hungry, and bug spray won't mean they'll never encounter pests. However, these tools provide support in making the hike possible for the hiker.

Now imagine a hiker who wants to go a long distance on a tough trail, but this time, the hiker is completely naked and isn't carrying anything! This hiker is unsupported but will face all the same challenges of the hike—with the additional obstacle of completing the hike in the nude. Receiving support as a disabled person is much like giving clothing and supplies to that nude hiker. The support does not eliminate the challenges of the task, but it makes the challenging pieces manageable.

Sustainable accommodations don't originate with a goal of making a task easier. They come from the need to make those tasks attainable. As we all know, what is *fair* is not always what is *equal*.

Within constructs of social interaction, it's time for both autistic people and neurotypical people to reframe how we think of disability accommodations. We need to generate reasonable modifications that are meaningful to the user. The world is not designed for naked hiking! We should all have access to the things that make the hike possible.

Chapter 15

Adulting

Leaving your childhood home for the first time is challenging for everyone. When you add autism to the mix, the adulting becomes even more complex. Lots of people initially leave home for college. Not me. The irony of speaking at universities across the country is that I don't have any personal experience with obtaining higher education. I might get asked to help faculty and students better understand challenges autistic learners face, but as a nontraditional learner, I've never experienced college. I wouldn't be accepted into most university settings because of academic challenges from my learning disabilities, dyscalculia, and memory issues. Accommodations are great, but for me, they haven't successfully helped me past third grade math.

Yet, while I may not have firsthand experience with a college environment, the first place where many people face adulthood, I sure do have experience with the challenges of adult life. I know what it's like to meet deadlines, manage my time, plan ahead, navigate various social environments, live with roommates, handle money, and care for both myself and my environment—all without the supervision of my mom. So far, I've survived … intact if not completely without injury.

Moving out of my mom's house and in with roommates was single-handedly the hardest thing I've ever done. In a matter of days, I became solely responsible for planning meals, going to the grocery store, preventing conflict with my roommates, tidying, scheduling appointments, and handling my own emotions when I had a rough time at work. I had a very limited amount of experience with any of these issues, but, through a few years of trial and lots of error, my roommates and I have developed systems which mostly mitigate challenges. Key word: *mostly*.

The Sunday Routine: the demise of best-laid plans

In the few minutes between kitchen cleanup and bedtime, nobody can personally stop a war on the other side of the globe. I know such things! But having the intellectual knowledge doesn't always help me through home routines when an intense desire to do the undoable gets control of my mind. Recently, I experienced a case in point while trying to manage a typical Sunday evening. You see, Sundays and I are already not friends ... despite my having encountered one every week for my entire life! It's that autism thing again.

One of the systems I have developed to combat my weekly crisis and promote sanity for me and those around me is The Sunday Routine. On Sundays my roommates and I prepare for the week ahead which includes all the following:

- planning meals for the week,

- selecting which meals will be eaten on which day,

- deep cleaning the kitchen,

- going to the grocery store,

- discussing evening activities for the week,

- running errands,

- cleaning my room,

- washing my hair,

- planning social media content, and

- packing my bag with everything I'll need at work

Making time to get a jumpstart on my responsibilities for the week gives me a chance to get a clear picture of the week ahead. That said, The Sunday Routine is not entirely foolproof. If the variables change too much, I run into problems. I struggle if my roommate isn't home when it's time to start making this to-do list, if the house is extra messy, if I'm missing information about my schedule, or if someone needs to make an alteration to the schedule I've created. Sometimes I just lack the motivation to tackle my list.

When challenges arise, I have a fairly robust skill repertoire I can use for problem solving. I know how to ask others for help. I can take a break when I need one. I can switch tasks if I get tired of the one I'm working on. I can wait until someone is available to help. But sometimes the stars in the sky of existential dread align just right and the results really throw me off my groove. I'll usually try to solve the problem in the ways I know, but when those attempts are unsuccessful, my brain initiates a meltdown.

When I arrive at that point, I need help to reduce the sense of overwhelm that autistic folks can experience. Sometimes help comes in the form of recruiting extra hands to help distribute household labor. Sometimes I need to borrow extra brain cells to help prioritize tasks, organize information, and make decisions. And, sometimes, I need a friend to provide distraction from the intellectual terrorism that I have imposed upon myself.

A few Sundays ago, the stars aligned. I was behind on laundry. I couldn't find the pasta salad I planned to pack for lunch. I needed to wash and dry my hair, feed the dog, pack my bag for work, clean my room, and put away the dishes—all before bedtime, which for me is 12 am. The problem was … it was already 10 pm, and I felt completely overwhelmed. You know what I did to help that situation? I watched videos on TikTok. In the process of my doom scrolling, I came across a video giving an update on the atrocities taking place in Gaza. That was the last straw for me. People are getting exploded and I'm overwhelmed about laundry? Angry with myself for the ongoing ridiculousness of the situation, my arm thought it would be a great idea to swipe all the decorative items from the table onto the floor without even consulting my brain first.

In response to feeling overwhelmed by numerous tasks, asking for help is a reasonable action step. However, due to the very nature of autism, the two necessary components—the ability to do the asking and having a close enough relationship with someone *to* ask—can be tricky. Lucky for me, while I don't have many friends, I am extremely close with the few I do have.

On the Sunday night of the table-sweeping, my roommate (yes, one of those close friends) eventually came to investigate after hearing the commotion of the decorative items hitting walls and floor. She asked me what happened, although she already knew. With tears running down my face, I said, "I made a mess."

She knew that, too. What she was really asking was why I was so upset.

I reluctantly launched into an explanation of why I was a horrible person for crying over household tasks when people on the other side of the world would love to be doing household tasks, but they can't anymore because their houses got blown up. What Rational Kaelynn already knew, but Upset Kaelynn needed a reminder about, was that no one ever came up with a solution for stopping war just a few hours before bedtime. Especially not when they had work the next morning.

This was a classic moment when logic and reason just weren't enough to talk down my emotions. Thankfully, my roommate had another strategy to offer: distraction. She suggested listening to music while finishing my tasks. Remembering I still needed to shower, she sang her own adult-themed rendition of *Rubber Ducky* in an effort to get me to laugh. And you know how I finished the tasks? While blasting the not-nearly-as-humorous original *Rubber Ducky* song.

Did I solve the conflicts in the Middle East? No. But I did wash my hair and pack my lunch, which is always a great first step for any person hoping to accomplish anything. All that to say, offering help with

problem-solving, organizing, or task completion can be helpful when someone is having a meltdown ... but if those things aren't working or aren't a realistic option, a simple distraction can be the fix we didn't know we needed.

I met my roommate at Project Hope Foundation where we're both employed providing behavioral therapy. She's trained to use these strategies just as I am. But it's worth noting that you don't need to be a therapist to learn to help. Besides that, just because you are a therapist (like me!) doesn't mean you'll have all the answers to your own problems.

Having just one person who is there for you, who understands you, or who is at least willing to *try* to understand and offer support can be a major contribution to success. This is true for all people, not just for those with autism. But it's worth emphasizing because those of us with autism may both require additional support and not know how to find it. We may need assistance to locate that one person.

My Person: an overlooked support role

Through the years I have been fortunate to have someone (more like a series of someones) outside my family and outside my educational setting with whom I've built a strong relationship to provide autism-related support. Over time, I developed a habit of naming and titling these people as My Person. My Person was always someone who knew me really well. The one holding the current My Person title has changed multiple times. Each time, My Person provided the support I needed no matter where I was in my journey.

While in high school at one of Project Hope Foundation's programs, Hope Academy, I did an internship with a goal that, after graduation, I could work for the organization as a therapist. The internship included a daily 30-minute period of paid time in which I practiced supervising a group of young children during recess. Along with some other high school students and a few staff, I'd facilitate group games, provide individualized attention to those who needed it, and see that bathroom needs were met. When time was up, my next event was lunch. Being the predictable kind of autistic person that I am, I always walked the same route back to my classroom. Out the door, down the stairs, turn left, through the parking lot, turn right, down the next set of stairs, and then a right turn into the building.

One day just as I made it down that first set of steps, someone suddenly came up from behind. I spun to see who it was and was relieved to see it was My Person.

"I'm headed to lunch," I told her.

"I know," she responded. "Let's walk this way today." She pointed to the right.

I considered this briefly, then said, "Nah, I'm good." I turned to the left, heading the direction I normally would, partly because that was my preference and partly to test if she was being playful or if she actually meant it.

"It's good to practice your flexibility," she said. She put her arm around my shoulders, gently tugging me right instead.

Despite feeling a low level of anxiety about turning the wrong direction, I leaned my body into hers, changing the shoulder tugging into more of a side hug. As the two of us walked together (from my perspective, still the *wrong* way), I protested ... sort of playfully, but with a twinge of seriousness, "Why are we doing this??"

"It's good for you!" she said.

She used to say that—almost as much as my mom—about things I didn't want to do.

Reflecting on such episodes as an adult, I see that My Person ... and my mom ... were usually right. I had to work hard to overcome elements of psychological rigidity.

While the statement "Be flexible" wasn't particularly useful in and of itself, choosing small elements to focus on one at a time definitely was helpful. As much as I hated it, specific practice opportunities at a controlled, low level helped diminish the degree of attachment I had for certain events/routines/sequences.

Since I attended a school for kids on the autism spectrum, I quickly learned that "Be flexible" is the phrase teachers and therapists used to let kids know when things were about to take an unexpected turn. It wasn't until years later that I put together that rigidity, or the need for sameness, is one of the defining characteristics of autism. The opposite of psychological rigidity is psychological flexibility! So when they told kids to "Be flexible," they were encouraging them to work through the rigidity that automatically comes with an autism diagnosis and can interfere with life.

I have strengths in language, both receptive and expressive, and even I couldn't decipher this roundabout sort of encouragement until adulthood. For many years I just thought it was a softer, more polite way of saying "I know what you want, but for some reason (whether it's genuinely unavailable or maybe just for some controlled practice), it's not happening." As I now work on this skill with my own clients, I frequently remember and try to imitate how My Person nudged me along my trail of progress.

For some people Their Person is a teacher who just gets them. For others, that role might be filled by a coach, or a mentor, or even a peer. In the context of this discussion, Your Person (or Your Child's Person) is someone outside your family who can provide extra support and guidance. This position might have an official capacity like a therapist, but oftentimes it comes about more organically.

In my experience, I don't choose My Person. They usually pick me. I like to joke that while I can be a pain in the ass, I do have many redeeming qualities that seem to draw in the right people if they stick around long enough.

It's worth a clarifying statement that in no case should any family or autistic person expect a current or recent therapist to be personally involved in family mechanics or your life outside the clinic. All professionals work under specific restrictions about personal involvement. That's for protection of clients' privacy, so the boundary always has to be maintained.

Even in my post-school years—perhaps especially since then—My Person(s) taught me a great deal. I often thought she knew how my brain worked better than I did. She became an important source for me to learn to manage and grow my executive skills. In another person's world, what Their Person might recognize and emphasize could be very different. But regardless of the focal point on any aspect of life, access to an excellent, concerned adult, outside of a parent, can provide relief and perspective not just for an autistic person but for an entire family.

While it might be one thing for a teenager or adult to recognize such a relationship, it gets far more complex for parents to create such engagement for their children. Parents may need to invest substantial time and effort into finding a My Person for a child, and nobody should tell you it will be easy. But doing so can create a major, positive social step toward building connections, emotional feedback, and a broader base of support outside family. It's unlikely anyone will come knock on your door to volunteer. This is a matter of actively searching out and finding candidates. People, autistic or not, usually like each other better when they know more about each other. So this process has to start where any friendship starts: getting to know more about new people.

Here are some steps that might help in finding a My Person candidate.

- Identify the trusted person/people in your life, or your child's life, who can provide support and feedback.

- Have straightforward discussion with the person about their willingness to be involved and to what extent.

- Keep your list fluid and stay alert for new candidates. It's easy for one person to burn out. Besides that, life circumstances—illness, family problems, a job switch—could change anyone's availability on short notice. Multiple people involved will reduce the impact if someone has to lessen their role.

- If they answer yes, determine how often is comfortable and appropriate to check in with them.

- Determine the easiest ways to check in and/or solicit input: Conversation? Phone? Email? Text?

- Once you've established who is willing to help and what works best for all, set reminders to establish engagement on a regular basis.

- Most importantly, thank them! Frequently!

- Finally, be understanding and gracious when and if they need to give up the role. And then go back to step one and identify some new candidates.

I acknowledge I am speaking from a position of privilege. Not everyone will be able to find someone to fill this role. And sometimes the My Person may need to serve as support for the parent/caregiver because it is not yet possible to build that relationship with the autistic person.

My Council of Affection: an employment strategy

I think the idea of My Person can be modified to become a helpful tool for assisting autistic adults maintain employment. As noted before, after graduation Project Hope Foundation hired me to provide autism services in their therapy program. Key to my success was the unofficial provision of what I lovingly called a Council of Affection. This was a group of three to five supervisors—depending on all of their personal schedules and their various maternity leaves! Project Hope leadership recognized the value I could bring to autism services but also understood that I would need extra help to bring my professional skills up to par with my clinical skills.

If you are in a support role, here are a few things you might consider offering to those you work with:

- weekly check-in meetings,

- personal goal setting,

- measuring progress and modifying as needed, and

- personal advocacy.

The supervisors who made up the Council of Affection were not only in my corner, rooting for my success, but they also took measures to help me achieve my goals. Depending on which of them were available, I'd schedule the meetings to discuss a range of topics like these:

- responding to various emails (politely),

- troubleshooting issues with co-workers when they came up,

- making clinical suggestions (politely),

- troubleshooting barriers to completing administrative tasks, and/or

- responding (politely) to a co-worker who isn't following company rules.

As you might imagine, the "politely" part was often challenging!

These weekly sessions were a chance to get additional support with solving problems and practicing soft skills. We've all written an email that might have sounded just a little too spicy. We've all asked a friend to read that email first before we hit send. We've all needed to vent about people causing issues at school or work. We've all had to ask for advice on how to handle tricky situations.

Yet, the check-ins filled a somewhat different role for me than what anyone might do with a family member or close friend.

- For one thing, they were reliable. If one member of my support team, or Council of Affection, didn't have the time or energy to meet with me, I could schedule with someone else and still get my needs met.

- For another, they cared about me, but from a supervisor or mentor perspective. We don't have to take all the advice our friends offer us. With the advice coming from a supervisor, I knew that what they said was in alignment with company policy, keeping me out of trouble.

- Finally, it wasn't a two-way street. The road went only one direction, and I was the only car. In other words, in the same way you don't need to return the question "How are you?" when you're in talk therapy, I didn't need to worry about balancing the time to listen to their thoughts and feelings the way I would have needed to with a family member or friend. The sole purpose of these one-hour weekly meetings was to increase my success.

It's important to recognize that other people on the autism spectrum may experience more challenges with language, which could complicate their ability to benefit as I have from a similar weekly check in. Additionally, difficulty with self-awareness, prioritization, and the ability to plan ahead may also create added challenges. If you're the employer trying to mitigate some of those barriers, structure your questions in a way that leads the person you're supporting toward the most insightful answer.

To recap for potential employers, a Council of Affection:

- needs several people to ensure availability,

- does not require social reciprocity,

- is available for in-person appointments (not just text or email),

- is well-versed in company policy, and

- consists of people who have strong, genuine interest in the autistic person's success.

Want to know the very best, most fun part about Councils of Affection? Nine years later, I'm now *on* one! It's gratifying to be part of a routine that's mentoring an up-and-coming young autistic man with aspirations to work at Project Hope Foundation. Hopefully in another few years, he'll be teaching others to do what he is now learning.

Part 5: My Personal FAQ

Questions can be weird and quirky dilemmas for autistic people. That's true for almost all of us, and possibly somewhat worse for me than average. Since my *Love On the Spectrum* era, I've been extremely outspoken about my autism, ADHD, and learning disabilities. Even years later, I haven't fully adjusted to the reality that anyone in the world can google my name and get a glimpse into my medical history.

I've written blog posts, been interviewed by national news, and had several videos go viral on different platforms, all referencing my experiences. I no longer have privacy regarding my struggles, as I've shared them for the world to hear. And that's okay. I am fully aware of the consequences of what I signed up for—even though it's sometimes horribly uncomfortable to have someone I just met ask invasive questions right after I just learned their first name.

An interesting thing, though ... because of so many questions—and how often they happen—it's become pretty easy for me to know what the hot button autism topics are. They shift around a little over time, but in the last year or two, we definitely have a few all-time winners in the "Frequently Asked Questions" competition.

When one person asks you a question, it's pretty safe to assume others want to know the same information. When a few dozen people per month ask the same questions, usually either in my social media comments or after a speaking engagement somewhere, then I can be sure it's totally safe to assume that many others also want that information. This section could be a whole book of its own, but I'm going to focus on the four questions I'm getting asked the most often.

Chapter 16

"What's all the mumbo jumbo about diagnostic levels?"

Origins and Overview

As I mentioned in Chapter 3, the 2013 update of the diagnostic criteria for autism introduced a three-tier system as a modifier to an autism diagnosis. The goal was to identify the level of support an autistic person requires based on their strengths and weaknesses. Anyone diagnosed with autism spectrum disorder after the update should also receive a modifier.

- Level One: "Requiring support"

- Level Two: "Requiring substantial support"

- Level Three: "Requiring very substantial support"

I also mentioned that some people have raised concerns about the use (or mis-use) of the modifiers. For example, families have worried that a Level Three modifier might be used as a barrier for receiving services. Providers might say that they work only with Levels One and Two. I can understand that concern, although I think many providers limited the scope of their practices long before the modifiers were in place.

In the social media world, I sometimes see the levels misused as a modifier of a particular mood or scenario. "I am usually Level One but today was full of sensory overload and conflict with my partner, so I had a meltdown and became Level Two." The modifiers are meant to be a global view of overall needs which would not change from moment to moment. That said, with effective therapies over time, people's support needs can improve from one level to another.

To try to explain the differences between needing "support," "substantial support," and "very substantial support," the DSM-5 includes some examples of each. Their examples frustrate me because they're trying to give generalized descriptions that intentionally avoid specific examples, as those would not be applicable to everyone. But on the flip side, they've been so vague that many readers struggle to understand which examples might fit inside each level.

At the risk of sounding older than I am, I've seen a lot of autism in my day—which is to say I've personally observed hundreds of autism manifestations. I'm not a doctor, but using my personal and clinical experience, I'm going to provide a few examples for each level. Repeat: I am *not* a doctor or diagnostician, and these additions are not official in any way. But I hope the context will help others better understand what might be present.

Unfortunately, if you're in the United States and were diagnosed before 2013 (like me), you didn't receive a support needs distinction in your diagnostic paperwork. And to be clear, if you have assigned yourself a level, I'm not going to fight you, a person I've never met before. I am fully aware that ranking ourselves based on needs and ability levels as it relates to our capacity to move through a world that wasn't built for us does indeed feel a bit like a dystopian Pokémon battle. *However* ... I'm going to offer some additional perspective I've had the privilege of obtaining through my clinical experience.

Level One: "Requiring support"

> "Social communication
>
> Without supports in place, deficits in social communication cause noticeable impairments. Difficulty initiating social interactions, and clear examples of atypical or unsuccessful responses to social overtures of others. May appear to have decreased interest in social

interactions. For example, a person who is able to speak in full sentences and engages in communication but whose to-and-fro conversation with others fails, and whose attempts to make friends are odd and typically unsuccessful.

Restricted, repetitive behaviors

Inflexibility of behavior causes significant interference with functioning in one or more contexts. Difficulty switching between activities. Problems of organization and planning hamper independence." (DSM-5, American Psychiatric Association 2013)

Level One Social Communication

Let's start with that first part, focusing on the DSM-5 language. *"Difficulty initiating social interactions, and clear examples of atypical or unsuccessful responses to social overtures of others."* This refers to folks having difficulty starting and continuing social interactions. The difficulty can include not knowing how to begin or join an interaction, or making an attempt to connect with others but that attempt doesn't end in the desired outcome.

Here's what that looks like for me: everyone in the office is talking about a topic I either know about or can contribute to (dogs, weekend plans, travel, etc.). I like to joke that I work in a neurodiversity-affirming bubble. Everyone I work with is wonderful … but the real world exists right outside our doors. Even in the context of my wonderful little bubble, I still struggle to generate a statement that allows me to join the conversation. Group conversations tend to move so quickly that by the time I've come up with an appropriate thing to say, the topic has already shifted.

Alternatively, I've also had the experience of saying the first thing that comes to mind during casual group conversation … and quickly realized it was the wrong thing to say because it didn't go over how I hoped it would. Maybe I've interjected with an opinion that wasn't asked for or was perceived as being extreme given the context. In my privileged experience as a conventionally attractive white girl, most people are polite when I do this, but I often have a hard time steering the conversation in a group of my peers and, therefore, furthering my connection with them.

Here are a few more examples of challenges we autistic people regularly face:

- not using eye contact to signal interest in conversation/attention;

- difficulty thinking of ways to contribute to conversation or interactions;

- over sharing or providing sensitive information regardless of the social context;

- giving too little information, making it difficult for interaction to continue;

- using offensive language or humor to initiate interaction;

- avoiding conversations with more than one person at a time;

- presenting body language, facial expressions, or intonation that suggests a person is uninterested in the conversation when approached by another person, regardless of their true level of interest;

- demonstrating intolerance for discussing subjects outside areas of interest;

- dominating conversation, not giving others an equal chance to speak; or

- frequently correcting others when they make insignificant mistakes such as mispronouncing a word, forgetting a detail in a story, singing the wrong lyrics to a song, etc.

Level One Restricted, Repetitive Behaviors

Now, let's look at the restricted/repetitive behavior aspect of someone with Level One support needs. *"Inflexibility of behavior causes significant interference with functioning in one or more contexts. Difficulty switching between activities. Problems of organization and planning hamper independence."*

For me personally, this is an area that I didn't realize how much I struggled with until I moved out of my mom's house and in with roommates. I have my own list of flexibility issues.

- I eat certain foods based only on the weather or my physical locations. For example, there are certain fruits I've designated as "work fruits" that can be eaten at work. There are also certain fruits that are "home fruits," that *obviously*, must only be eaten at home!

- Every light in the house is used based on the time of day. The nightstand lamp is to be used only at night (after sunset), the dresser lamp is used only in the morning (before I've left the house for the first time that day). The kitchen lights remain on from the time dinner starts and I turn them off only after the dishes have been done and my lunch has been packed for work.

- I use my laptop only in some rooms and my iPad or phone in other rooms.

- As I mentioned earlier in this book, I'd rather drive 40 minutes to use the office at work rather than use the one at my house because driving to work is my routine.

- There are certain activities (usually video editing or writing) I do only when alone in my room for several hours because I don't like to be interrupted and am trying to keep myself from verbally lashing out at others for distracting me. In doing this, I often struggle with interrupting myself and reaching a stopping point when it's time to do something else.

This should go without saying, but if I'm saying it anyway, there's a reason: each person's struggle with flexibility will look different. While I make lots of seemingly unnecessary rules for myself to follow, they don't completely interfere with my ability to function. In my own mind, I can defend them by describing all the reasons they're practical. But that's my point: I suspect everyone on the spectrum could do the same about their own rules if they possessed enough language capabilities. Everyone has preferences or ideas about what is the right way to do something. But *not* everyone needs to follow these often self-made and self-enforced rules in order to be okay. If an alteration in a routine or expectation regularly causes significant distress, that may be a noteworthy example of an autistic trait.

Level Two: "Requiring substantial support"

"Social communication

Marked deficits in verbal and nonverbal social communication skills; social impairments apparent even with supports in place; limited initiation of social interactions; and reduced or abnormal responses to social overtures from others. For example, a person who speaks simple sentences, whose interaction is limited to narrow special interests, and who has markedly odd nonverbal communication.

Restricted, repetitive behaviors

Inflexibility of behavior, difficulty coping with change, or other restricted/repetitive behaviors appear frequently enough to be obvious to the casual observer and interfere with functioning in a variety of contexts. Distress and/or difficulty changing focus or action." (DSM-5, American Psychiatric Association 2013)

Level Two Social Communication

Let's really pick apart what these things mean in real life. When they say *marked deficits,* they mean that it's immediately obvious to everyone. This would imply that masking one's challenges related to verbal and nonverbal social communication skills would be almost impossible. In terms of everyday behavior, here's what it might look like to have *"marked deficits in verbal and nonverbal social communication skills"* might look like:

- communicating requests with one word or short sentences;

- grabbing or touching others regardless of relationship type (strangers, acquaintances, community helpers, friends, family, etc.) to initiate social interactions in place of more traditional communication;

- repeating words or phrases said by others without understanding the context;

- problems with literal interpretation of figurative language so that slang like "You're on fire today" may cause genuine confusion;

- difficulty understanding personal space boundaries or invading the personal space of others regardless of context;

- not noticing or responding to others' crying, laughing, body language, or facial expressions;

- frequently interrupting conversations or games due to a lack of understanding about taking turns;

- preferring to stim alone for significant periods of time;

- sometimes ignoring others even when directly addressed; or

- needing direct instruction to understand and use prepositions, pronouns, and who/what/when/where/why questions.

Remember that the second part of that definition is *"social impairments apparent even with supports in place."* This means that even in the context of having access to accommodations and a supportive environment, social and communication difficulties will still present challenges. As someone who has never struggled to acquire verbal communication, I can't imagine how frustrating it must be to have something to say, but not have enough language skills to be able to say it the way I want to. When a person has to navigate communication challenges to this degree, accommodations and alternative forms of communication can be a great help. That said, it's important to know that with this Level Two distinction, tools are helpful, but they don't completely address the barriers. Even with the use of tools and accommodations, the social communication differences a person experiences are still overtly obvious.

Level Two Restricted, Repetitive Behaviors

Here are some examples of how Level Two restricted/repetitive behavior might apply to someone's life:

- using same toys in repeated patterns and resisting the addition of new actions, words, phrases, or themes, such as lining up toys, then picking up each toy and running up and down the hall a specific number of times, making a particular sound, before returning to repeat with next toy;

- rejecting novel ways of playing games or any adjustment to rules, such as being unwilling to simplify games for younger or inexperienced players;

- insisting on sameness in group games (using the same game pieces, taking turns in the same order, standing in the same spot) and remaining unreceptive to others' attempts to negotiate changes;

- becoming significantly distressed if driving/walking route is altered for any reason, possibly engaging in dangerous behavior like hitting others or head banging if road construction requires a detour;

- perseverating or getting stuck on small changes, even if they've already happened, such as repetitively talking about a substitute teacher even if that happened last week and the regular teacher has returned;

- difficulty accepting when others change aspects of their own routine or physical appearance;

- experiencing frequent meltdowns if friends or family members want to eat at a new restaurant, watch a new movie, or go to a new place;

- wearing the same clothes every day and rejecting alternatives even if the clothes are soiled and need to be washed;

- refusing to participate in activities unless all aspects are predictable and remain unaltered;

- crying, screaming, or running away when offered new activities;

- stimming so frequently that it prohibits their ability to direct their focus elsewhere; or

- stimming with such intensity that safety is compromised, such as not being able to pause finger flicking/rapid blinking/spinning long enough to look both ways before crossing the street.

I'd like to draw your attention to this particular wording: *"restricted/ repetitive behaviors appear frequently enough to be obvious to the casual observer and interfere with functioning in a variety of contexts."* In a perfect world, no one would have to conceal the things that make them different, but you don't need me to tell you that our world is anything but perfect. The truth is, while no one should have to hide parts of themselves, the ability to do so is a privilege, and it's one that not everyone has.

Level Three: "Requiring very substantial support"

"Social communication

Severe deficits in verbal and nonverbal social communication skills cause severe impairments in functioning, very limited initiation of social interactions, and minimal response to social overtures from others. For example, a person with few words of intelligible speech who rarely initiates interaction and, when he or she does, makes unusual approaches to meet needs only and responds to only very direct social approaches.

Restricted, repetitive behaviors

Inflexibility of behavior, extreme difficulty coping with change, or other restricted/repetitive behaviors markedly interfere with functioning in all spheres. Great distress/difficulty changing focus or action." (DSM-5, American Psychiatric Association 2013)

Level Three Social Communication

Lastly, because we're going in numerical order, let's talk about Level Three autism, which is something more people should do in general. If I were to channel my inner Barack Obama, I'd tell you in a "Yes we can" fueled passion that the autism community *should* be able to unite our pursuit of accommodations and social acceptance for this group who can't independently ask for policy changes. Unfortunately, it's not in my nature to maintain that sort of optimism. Instead, the realist in me would like to propose that you at least pay close attention to what Level Three autism can look like, even if it doesn't impact your daily life.

Someone may not relate to my personal challenges, but it's comforting when they at least listen with the intention of understanding.

Here are examples of what *"[s]evere deficits in verbal and nonverbal social communication skills"* can mean in day-to-day life:

- is potentially non-speaking, unable to use verbal communication effectively;

- needs several years of intense instruction to learn to use alternative communication systems such as a speech generating device, picture cards, or sign language;

- uses only one word at a time or fragmented sentences to communicate basic needs regardless of their communication system, such as using only a single icon to convey a message: "pretzels";

- struggles to use and understand certain language concepts such as proper syntax, grammar, and tense;

- does not understand and/or use gestures such as pointing, waving, nodding, etc.;

- needs instructions to be limited to only key words ("Get your shoes" rather than "Why don't you grab your shoes and we can head to the park?");

- uses short phrases or sounds to convey specific meanings that are often unclear or seem out of context to outsiders, such as saying, "The ants go marching one by one" instead of "I'm ready to go home"; or

- struggles with pronunciation and articulation, making it difficult for unfamiliar people to understand speech.

In exploring the other part of the Level Three language, *"very limited*

initiation of social interactions, and minimal response to social overtures from others,"
I want to emphasize the modifiers *"very limited initiation"* and *"minimal*
response." While all of us autistic people experience social motivation
differently from neurotypical folks, the degree to which it affects a
person's life increases with the levels. Here are some examples of what
"very limited initiation of social interactions, and minimal response to social overtures
from others" can look like:

- no response when greeted by others, including close family and friends;

- little acknowledgment when others initiate conversation or ask a question;

- ignores assistance or direction when someone offers to help with participating in various activities;

- becomes upset/emotionally dysregulated when someone suggests an activity in which they don't want to participate;

- even when presented with social opportunities in inclusive settings, often prefers to sit out/be left alone, not responding to the invitation in any way;

- no attempt to share interests with others;

- no response when someone else attempts to share their interests;

- often struggles to tolerate preferences of others, such as not allowing family members to select TV shows, leisure activities, or seating options;

- often becomes upset/emotionally dysregulated when asked to share space with others (company over at the house, people gathered in a single location, group settings);

- sometimes uses yelling, screaming, pushing, hitting, throwing, disrobing, and/or inappropriate sexual behavior to get others to leave them alone or give them increased personal space;

- no engagement in back-and-forth conversation on any topic; or

- rarely gains simple skills through observation alone, such as a demonstration of hand washing, therefore requiring additional instruction.

Level Three Restricted, Repetitive Behaviors

And lastly, this is what the DSM-5 says restricted/repetitive behaviors look like for Level Three autism: *"Inflexibility of behavior, extreme difficulty coping with change, or other restricted/repetitive behavior markedly interfere with*

functioning on all spheres. Great distress/difficulty changing focus or action." Here's what that looks like in everyday life:

- insists on an exact sequence of daily activities and experiences severe distress if any part is altered, such as requiring a specific morning routine (e.g., brushing teeth, eating breakfast, dressing) and becomes extremely distressed if breakfast is delayed or skipped, resulting in a complete inability to proceed with the rest of the day;

- needs objects placed in a precise order, becoming highly agitated if order is disturbed;

- exhibits extreme anxiety or panic (screaming/throwing oneself onto the floor/aggression toward others/self-injury) in response to minor changes in environment or routine;

- experiences significant meltdowns when transitioning from one activity to another;

- stims to a degree that makes other activities impossible;

- repeats words or phrases constantly, interrupting conversations and daily functioning; or

- engages in loud, repetitive behaviors like verbal stimming in public places such as restaurants or parks, drawing significant attention and distressing others, often resulting in being asked to leave.

Questions, concerns, and objections about diagnostic levels create a nearly endless stream of controversy. To me, most of the discussion results either from incorrect interpretation or a lack of understanding the clinical need. If you're trying to understand your own autism, that's one thing. If a parent is trying to understand a child's (or even multiple children's), that's another. But for those of us out here trying to develop—and pay for—appropriate plans to assist dozens, scores, or even hundreds of clients, there has to be a framework through which we can understand not only the needs of the individual, but also have a system for communicating among professionals: therapeutic, medical, insurance providers, etc. The levels system isn't a perfect one, but it's what we have at the moment. In a professional context, levels have nothing to do with mood or a day of tough circumstances … and everything to do with providing the support individuals need.

Chapter 17

"What am I looking for in a therapist?"

If you're a parent debating therapy options for your child, what you decide absolutely will shape the future in every possible way. Let's go through some of the most important considerations.

For starters, let's be sure we're discussing the same concept. In this context of discussing autism, the term *therapy* means professionally targeting and removing barriers to life's opportunities in measurable ways.

Parents who are confronted with a new autism diagnosis face huge decisions. What they decide about therapy and education will profoundly affect their children for life. Yet anyone starting that journey will quickly discover that any discussion of any kind of therapy runs headfirst into some of the most intense autism controversy that exists. Endless debates rage about who needs therapy, when, and why. The internet overflows with commentary from those who believe they were harmed by therapy. The cost and logistics of therapy often overwhelm parents. Depending on where an autistic person is on the spectrum, it's easy to wonder why, or if, therapy is necessary at all.

"Who needs therapy and why?"

Why do autistic kids need therapy? I was the child without a diagnosis who could have benefited from therapy. I was the teenager who received badly needed therapy. I'm also the adult who has seen the therapy I now provide for others vastly improve their quality of life. So here's what I know to be true.

As a starting point, when a good therapist sets out to help an autistic person, here is what we're *not* doing:

- making them appear "normal";

- "catching them up" to neurotypical peers; or

- "fixing/changing" who they are.

Here's what a good therapist should be doing: teaching them skills that will help them remove the barriers they face because of their diagnosis.

Let's rephrase: Why do children need therapy? The short answer: so they can take full advantage of every opportunity that comes their way!

"What are the signs of a good therapist?"

So with a better idea in mind of your objectives and how you plan to achieve them, how exactly does one go about locating The Mythical Beast … a professional therapist who will help achieve said goals? As a really basic starting point, let's note some considerations for choosing a therapy provider.

- Good providers not only to accept feedback, but they actively seek it out. They welcome feedback from their peers and autistic advocates. They seek feedback from the people with whom they're working.

- High-quality providers help their clients with skills that the clients want to learn. Providers should select goals that directly relate to removing barriers their clients face day to day.

- A provider worth your attention will make changes to their own behavior to meet clients' individual needs. Modifications might include adjustments to the physical environment, altering a teaching style, and personalizing immediate areas of focus. Be careful about providers who select goals based only on a certain standard or curriculum.

- Any relationship will have conflict, but you need conflict to be minimal with your provider. Note that there is a difference between a provider who regularly offers challenge and one who perpetually engages in conflict.

This is certainly not a complete list. But for an actionable list, start with those four points above. Then think about your loved one—or yourself—to personalize your own list *before* you talk to any prospective therapist. Take it with you to your early appointment or assessment. Refer to it. Stick to it!

"Why do therapists sometimes seem impersonal?"

You won't go far researching any kind of therapy—or provider—before you encounter what's referred to as professional boundaries. Therapists have to stay objective. They have to keep personal matters separate from their work. This requirement is a valid need, but it's more nuanced than many assume.

In my opinion, one of the more actionable criticisms of any therapy is the artificial approach that can arise in our relationships with clients and families. I recognize the necessity of professional boundaries. Dual relationships are unethical, and nobody should enter a therapeutic relationship expecting the therapist to become your closest friend.

Yet, I still have a problem with the reality that therapists, especially in the behavior analyzing field, are often notorious for coming across as detached. Not everyone will be the "warm and fuzzy" type. That's okay because that's not the expectation. But it is fair to expect therapists to lead with humanity when providing *human* services.

Let's address the other side of the dilemma. Speaking on behalf of the therapists, it's easy to turn off those more human parts of ourselves because the entire professional field places such a heavy emphasis on staying objective. Our ability to be objective in certain circumstances is part of what makes our field both unique and valuable. The caveat here is that objectivity without nuance can lead to a kind of detachment which inadvertently harms the human beings we set out to help.

When people struggle with connection and human relationships, it seems counterintuitive to try to teach them from behind a self-made wall of objectivity. Ethical restrictions for therapists do not prohibit us from

forming reciprocal relationships with those we serve. As my mother likes to say, "Relationships take work." I often hear this statement in direct contradiction of my wish to dismiss or avoid someone with whom I've had some conflict. In my world, this famous parental statement is the introduction to a certain lecture that I've received countless times about how important it is to work through challenging situations. It's one of those practical sermons you hear and immediately know there's nothing you can say to counter it reasonably. In other words, my mother is always right. Thanks, Mom!

Chapter 18

"What do you think about ABA?"

To quote Shrek, "I'm an ogre. Grab your torch and pitchfork." In my role as an ABA therapist, I've seen the pitchforks! In the entire world of autism, I don't know of any topic more controversial than *Applied Behavior Analysis* (ABA), a skill-building therapy. Yet I know from personal experience, ABA also carries the power to improve individual lives tremendously and thereby also improve our collective future world. When I consider the enormity both of the controversy and value, I *can't* send out a book purporting to be about autism—understanding it, coping with it, helping those who have it—unless I also share some perspective and experience about ABA. I've used the science for a while now. And I happen to know I'm good at it. So I have things to say, and I hope you'll consider them with an open mind.

I have enough passion for the profession that I can simultaneously tell you all the reasons I believe ABA therapy is not only acceptable, but *needed* … and also be working on a second book geared toward blunt, actionable critique for ABA providers.

Parents, to you, especially, who are trying to make the best possible decisions for a young child, I hope you'll read this entire chapter and consider what's at stake. On the other hand, if you are reading this chapter in preparation for writing your persuasive essay damning me and my thoughts, I suggest you stick to journaling. That is not to say that I don't appreciate thoughtful criticism. I do. I read it and, in fact, seek it out. I pride myself on a balanced approach across all my interests, including ABA therapy. I hope that others will return the favor in consuming this content. Meanwhile, here are the factors I know to be true based on about a decade of training and practice.

"Is it true that some recipients report negative experiences from receiving ABA therapy?" Yes.

This might be where you'd expect to see a "but …," as in, "Yes, ABA has caused PTSD in some people, but …." I can assure you there won't be any "buts" here. Saying "Yes, but …" gets us nowhere. "Yes, but …" keeps us stuck in a loop where the solution is always just out of reach. Conversely, saying "Yes, *and* …" is the way to move forward. It acknowledges and accepts truths in pursuit of a solution.

If we say, "yes, ABA has caused trauma in some recipients, *but* it's not like that anymore;" or, "*but,* those were just bad therapists;" or, "*but,* that doesn't happen to most people;" then we would not only close ourselves off to the possibility of reform, but also neglect to take responsibility for the issue at hand.

"Is it true that ABA has evolved over time and certain methodologies are no longer considered best practice?" Yes.

If we say, "Yes, ABA used methodologies in the past that are no longer best practice *and* many dedicated folks are working tirelessly on promoting standards of practice based on valid research," we've given ourselves an opportunity to learn from our mistakes and uphold the value of ongoing improvement. We can acknowledge, examine, and use our yucky history as fuel to propel us all toward a better future.

This isn't a new idea. It's the same thing we did with outdated medical practices. We don't bleed people anymore. Nobody uses cocaine these days to treat hay fever. The same idea holds true for education. Today's schools don't discriminate based on race and teachers don't beat children for making spelling errors. We didn't ban the field of medicine and we didn't abolish public education. We acknowledged that some stuff *sucked,* and we are continuing to make efforts to improve.

The autism community at large has rightfully voiced concerns regarding

ABA's prioritization of behavioral outcomes over emotional health, the unnatural and sometimes degrading use of rewards, and the encouraged suppression of non-harmful autistic behaviors like stimming. Yes, those things are harmful. *And* they're not currently considered ethical practices by ABA providers.

"Is it true that ABA can be effective skill-building therapy for many on the spectrum?" Also, yes.

I have to answer this question from my dual perspective as both an autistic person and a therapist. From my position on the bridge between those worlds, I want to emphasize that ABA, when implemented ethically, is not only worthwhile but also potentially life-changing ... and ... in some cases, ABA is life*saving!* So let's take a closer look at some components that I love about ABA therapy:

- evidence-based effective principles;

- adaptability across environments;

- individualization to meet each client's needs; and

- commitment to ongoing improvement.

Evidence-Based Effective Principles

ABA therapy is based on behavioral principles, and behavioral principles work whether you believe in them or not. There's never been a reasonable or worthwhile debate on if behavioral principles *work*. We know, because, science! When we apply behavioral concepts (reinforcement, punishment, shaping, or chaining) to a living organism, anyone can observe a measurable shift in behavior. This has always been true and will always remain true.

In summary, behavioral principles are the opposite of Santa Claus. Santa stops coming when you stop believing in him. Behavioral principles still work even if you don't believe in them. As a living organism, so long as you continue to exist, you will still be bound by behavioral principles.

And before you jump into the "but I wouldn't be [this] if society wouldn't do [that]" argument, I hate to break it to you, but, yes, you would. In the history of the world, much like with the various laws of physics, humans have always *been* and will always *be* stuck with behavioral principles.

When you feel hungry, you eat food to make the feeling of hunger go away. When you step on a fire ant mound and get attacked, you move away quickly, trying to brush the ants off, and you probably will be more careful where you step next time. We observe these naturally occurring contingencies all around our world. We have to realize (understand and admit) that we're all more or less manipulated by behavioral principles. That was true for millennia before humans realized we could alter the contingencies to stack the odds in favor of our own preferred outcome. "*Can* a behavior be shifted?" will forever be the wrong question.

What are the right questions?

- "*Should* a behavior be shifted?"

- "Who gets to decide what a desirable outcome is?"

- And beyond that: "Which contingencies can be altered in order to achieve said desirable outcome?"

While I can't answer those questions for your unique circumstances, I can tell you that the field of ABA is working hard to be sure all those answers are based in ethics and research so that the outcomes always center on improving lives.

ABA therapy typically starts with many hours a week, based on each person's individual assessment. Why is the higher number of hours an advantage? Humans learn things through repetition. For autistic humans, as long as we're focused on skills meaningful both to us and our families, having sufficient chances to practice those skills can make the difference between gaining independence and having to rely on the support of another person.

Let me be clear: yes, we *all* need to rely on the support of other humans for certain things. Yet there are a number of activities in which needing support can actually increase someone's vulnerability. Total independence doesn't necessarily have to be the goal ... but safety should be. People who need assistance with personal care tasks like using the toilet, bathing, or dressing are automatically at an increased risk of sexual abuse. People who need support in managing finances, communicating their desires, or taking care of their general health (eating at regular intervals, indicating when something hurts, getting enough sleep, exercising) are at an increased risk of being taken advantage of. It should go without saying, but I'm going to say it anyway: those who need support to control aggressive or destructive impulses are at an increased risk of being unfairly restrained, physically abused, or experiencing high rates of daily coercion in failed attempts to help them regulate their behavior. So when we fold all those considerations into our context, we see the necessity of *practice*. When folks have more chances to practice crucial skills like self-care, emotional regulation, and communication, they're better equipped to build the repertoires required to keep themselves *safe*.

Adaptability Across Environments

A greatly under-appreciated aspect of ABA therapy comes from its adaptability. We've talked about the advantages of having more opportunities to practice skill building, but it's also important to pay attention to *where* those skills can be worked on.

Imagine for a minute that when faced with a challenging situation surpassing your human level of ability, you feel a nearly uncontrollable impulse to punch yourself repeatedly in the head. Maybe you don't encounter those situations often, but when you do, both you and the people around you feel utterly powerless to know what to do and how to make it better. The cool thing about ABA is that we don't have to confine your reactions to when or *if* the situation occurs. Instead, we can meet people where they are in the most literal sense.

For me, I'll remember one such situation for my entire life. "Where I was" was at my first OB-GYN appointment when I encountered that nearly irresistible impulse. Certainly I never wished for such an impulse, but there it was anyway. Lucky for both me and my mom, my therapist had predicted the impulse weeks before the appointment. By that, I mean she made plans to come with us to the appointment. ABA isn't confined to a clinic or a school; ABA is travel-sized. It can go where it's needed. In my case, I needed support that day at the doctor's office, not a few days before or after.

If I could scream it from the rooftops, I'd do so just to get people to hear me—same as I emphasized in Chapter 7 about meltdowns: *people cannot learn new skills or absorb information when they are experiencing an emotional or behavioral crisis.* So while my therapist had no intention of teaching me coping strategies while I was in the middle of punching my own head, she did plan on offering support and teaching when I was in a place actually to hear her. When I was settled and chill, we worked on filling out forms in the waiting room, giving information to the receptionist, and interacting with the nurses. While it can certainly be helpful to make a plan or discuss strategies beforehand (the way you might do in traditional talk therapy) practicing skill building in the context of real-world events is a very different kind of hands-on learning that can be more effective for some people.

The goal should always be to support people in such a way that they never reach that breaking point. But the world goes round, and the breaking points sometimes still do happen. As therapists, we try our hardest to provide folks with the tools they need to remain within their personal baseline level of emotional regulation. Taking breaks, using sensory tools, engaging with our special interests, and using coping strategies are all great ways to stay calm, but when extreme emotions or negative physical states are involved, sometimes those things just aren't enough to prevent a meltdown from happening.

Back in my own example, the very nature of the appointment itself brought me rapidly toward my own personal breaking point. My therapist, understanding the teaching opportunity she'd been capitalizing on just moments before had now ended, didn't say another word. She knew I couldn't receive information when in crisis. Instead, she joined my mom and the medical staff in helping me de-escalate so I could return to being in better control of my emotions and, therefore, my behavior.

I'll spare you the details of how this whole process went down from start to finish, but I hope you can appreciate—as I did then, and even far more so now—the adaptability of the service my therapist provided. Did we talk about the appointment both before and after? Of course. But personally, I think the most useful thing was having her there—when and where I actually needed her help the most. Autistic people who utilize special services don't need them just when we're in the office, the clinic, or school. If we need services, chances are, we'll eventually encounter those times of need outside of regularly scheduled sessions. ABA provides the flexibility to meet those areas of need exactly where and when they occur.

Although ABA providers can't always attend every stressful life situation with you, they should have the ability to attend *to* them. In other words, they should create plans for support and skill-building to make these situations as manageable as possible.

Individualization to Meet Each Client's Needs

My absolute favorite thing about ABA is our ability to take complex skills and break them down into consumable parts, designed to meet the particular needs of each specific client. You might question, "Isn't anyone who's trying to teach anything already doing that?" My answer: they should be, but likely aren't!

Let's use the task of learning to ride a bike as a case study. The use of training wheels is an almost-universal part of the process. Training wheels help people build muscle memory with the mechanics of moving a bike without being required to navigate all the other related complexities—like balance. And for most people, the process of learning to ride the bike really only involves two steps: (1) use training wheels, and (2) no more training wheels and we hope it all works out for you! To be fair, this process usually works since most people only *need* those two steps. But what about people who need more?

Too often, there is an all-or-nothing approach. If it looks like the learner might eventually figure it out, they're encouraged just to keep trying with the training wheels, over and over. If that doesn't produce success, we conclude that bike riding is just not in the cards for our learner.

The beauty of ABA—its very essence—is the inherent process of breaking things down into pieces suitable for the individual learner. People may assume the "analyzing behavior" part of ABA comes from analyzing autistic behavior. Not necessarily. It also means analyzing whatever elements are creating difficulty with achieving the goal.

Too often in traditional teaching environments, the breaking-down-into-pieces option is simply not extensive enough for autistic people. In effect, autistic learners are told, "If you can't chew the bites that were cut for you … you should either try chewing a little harder, or realize this meal isn't meant for you and spit it out." Give more effort or give up. ABA does not presume that you have the ability and are simply not trying, and ABA does not presume that a goal is beyond reach. ABA proposes a third option.

Option three involves breaking the skill down even further to increase a person's chances of success and then building it back together. When most of the rest of the world says "But training wheels are the first step!" ABA replies, "Wanna bet?" We *will* make riding a bike easier than tossing someone onto a bike with training wheels and hoping for the best.

So let's take our theoretical autistic person who really *wants* to learn to ride, and for whom that two-step training-wheels-and-off approach isn't enough. An effective ABA therapist is building a checklist.

- Does this autistic person *want* to learn to ride a bike?

- Does our learner know how to sit on the bike?

- Do they know where to put their hands?

- Do they know where their feet go?

- Can they make the pedals move?

- Do they understand how to move their hands (gently!) in the direction they want to go?

- Is their balance good enough to handle the bike, even with training wheels?

- Do they understand they have to keep moving or else put their feet back on the ground?

In ABA, these could all be separate pieces of knowledge, separate skills. Maybe people in the past have tried to help our autistic learner ride that bike. Maybe the instructor has demonstrated it, and then even tried physically helping our person move their feet with the pedals. Except success didn't happen because our learner quickly gets overwhelmed by trying to coordinate hands, arms, upper body, feet, and balance all at once. Effective ABA will isolate all those components, teach them individually, and then spend the time to put those components back together.

ABA starts with gaining an accurate assessment of our Hopeful Rider's current abilities, based on strategic observation rather than a default assumption. By comparing the checklist of needed skills against the assessment of our particular person's demonstrated skills, ABA would work to fill in the gaps by teaching the skills that are missing. This process would be individualized to meet the learner's specific needs. For some, we might need to start with where to place their hands and feet. For others, we might build muscle coordination, with dedicated practice while seated in a chair, using stationary pedals on the floor. As the person gains confidence and fluency with each component, we'll add other pieces. They might need to move from the chair to a stationary bike—no forward motion yet, but now our learner needs to understand how to sit while peddling. Then where to hold their hands while still peddling. Maybe then they're ready to return to the actual bicycle. Eventually—after perhaps a dozen separate stages of learning—they'll be ready for those training wheels … which are *step one* for a typical learner!

While not presuming ability, ABA does presume competence, a phrase that is important in the autism community. *Presume competence* is basically a polite way of saying "Don't treat people like they're idiots." The phrase becomes increasingly significant in the context of interacting with folks who struggle more intensely with verbal communication. Much of society starts with an underlying assumption these folks are incompetent based solely on their difficulty with words. The autism community often uses that phrase, presume competence, as a way to combat such assumptions.

I recognize that at first glance presume competence, which I'm advocating for, seems similar to presuming pre-existing knowledge, which I've cautioned against! In the realm of high quality ABA services, *presume competence* is more like *presume possibility*. We don't assume you can already ride the bike, but we do presume that it could be possible for you build the skill.

Commitment to Ongoing Improvement

The last point I'll offer in my support of ABA therapy is the field's commitment to ongoing improvement. I certainly understand that not every ABA practitioner embodies this value. However, the field itself is built on making data-driven decisions. Consequently, when the data reflects that a method is ineffective, harmful, or unnecessary, an adjustment is not only recommended, but required. Anyone who professes a commitment to ongoing improvement understands not only the need to tolerate criticism but also the duty to seek it out in various forms, from various perspectives.

Critique has come from members of the autism community. They have called on the field to "Listen to autistic voices" in making necessary adjustments. From my insider status as both an autistic person and an ABA therapist, I can assure you, that call is absolutely being answered. Methodology has been adjusted based on data—and adjustments will continue to happen as new data comes in. Sure, there really are providers who make excuses for why they "can't come to the phone right now." But take comfort in knowing that their phone will continue to ring.

I am often described by people who know me well as being the most pessimistic person anyone has ever met. Now, I don't know about all that, but I certainly do have a tendency toward being critical. On a personal level, I believe that truly loving something means helping it to flourish, and that will necessarily involve some straightforward criticism.

And so my love for this field of ABA means that I can serve as a cheerleader, including writing this chapter describing why I believe ABA is needed by so many, and also be a coach, already working on a second book giving feedback for providers.

When embodying the value of ongoing improvement, the statement "It's not like that anymore" doesn't move us forward until it moves *everyone* forward. The truth is, in some places, it *is* still like that. Even in this modern day and age, the state of medical treatment is deplorable in far too many places. Even in this modern day and age, educational equality is still just an ideal. Unfair punishment procedures are still utilized, and cultural suppression is still commonplace. Even in this modern day and age, some ABA therapists still discourage stims, require masking of any and all obvious signs of autism, and implement emotionally damaging teaching procedures. In summary, at the risk of crudeness: shit still happens.

But that fact returns me to my point: this field's commitment to data-driven practices will propel it forward in a trajectory of ongoing improvement. I plan to be part of that process!

Chapter 19

"How do I get involved in advocacy?"

I get some version of this coming my way every week: "Kaelynn, I'd love to get into autism advocacy. I'd like to help, but I don't know where to start. Do you have any suggestions?"

Yes! I sure do. I have lots of them. But my answer(s) might not be what you expect. I urge you to choose options that are actually helpful to autistic people.

Before you start making videos, or giving advice, or enlisting yourself in an online army to fight World War III in the comments section ... all because some autism mom used a puzzle piece emoji instead of the infinity sign to symbolize autism ... do a few other things first.

Get involved beyond social media. It's really that simple. If you're not autistic, you no doubt have some factors to learn. If you are autistic, keep in mind that your lived experience as an autistic person is *valid*, but your experience working with the community is *valuable!*

There are many opportunities for hands-on experience both in-person *and* online. But you'll need to spend some time and effort to find ones that align with your values, your schedule, and your budget. Here are a few.

- Tour a residential or therapeutic facility.

- Volunteer with a non-profit autism organization. Gain some personal knowledge and maybe even make an autistic friend or two.

- If your schedule doesn't allow the kind of volunteering they need, can you offer to purchase some supplies for their therapists, craft room, or activity center?

- Find a family directly affected by autism and offer your help. Who knows … you might end up turning yourself into an autistic kid's My Person.

- Simply offer companionship to those whose needs look different from your own, and that's especially true if you're on the spectrum yourself. Add yourself to the group of us who do our best to consider more ways that we, as a community, can work to include people of all ability levels, including those whose language abilities do not allow them to participate in social media.

- If you have the skills, provide respite care.

- Participate in research.

- Join an advisory committee.

- If you're an adult with the time and flexibility, you might want to consider offering to train as a volunteer for Court-Appointed Special Advocates (CASA). It's hard to get far through any news source anymore without reading about children in foster care, children suffering abuse, or any of dozens of other situations. Let your local group know you have a particular interest in autistic children.

If you have a position of influence or management in a business, school, or civic group, I have a suggestion for you that goes a little beyond a single bullet point. Give some thought—and then some action—to the idea of making that environment more friendly to autistic people and their families. The term *inclusion* is a little overworked these days, but I'm still going to use it because I can't think of a better one.

We hear a lot now about inclusion. But I wouldn't be doing my job with this book if I didn't point out that not everything happening in the name of inclusion is actually very beneficial to (or inclusive of!) autistic people and their families. All too often, both organizations and people will sometimes put forth minimal effort, yet claim they are maximally inclusive. It's common to hear, "Yes! We are inclusive" or to see a paragraph proclaiming it on a website. But simply adopting the term cannot be all that happens. Meaningful inclusion that results in improved lives is based on action, with specific, directed steps. The correct question is not "Are you inclusive?" but "What is it that makes you inclusive?"

Being open to feedback is critical. Out in the community, even more than online, I encounter organizations who have taken specific steps toward that goal of inclusivity. But sometimes when I interact with their autistic people, I see that the steps are not really helping very much. We need for people in positions of authority to listen when autistic people involved say, "I appreciate the effort, but could we try this other thing?"

The response to valid critique can differentiate between whether the commitment is to improving a corporate image or improving actual lives. Are they open to additional steps? Willing to make some revisions? Or do they get offended and double down with more statements about what they're already doing?

I'll tell you one more practice—unfortunately increasingly common— that many of us autistic people really (really!) dislike. I've lost count how many times I've heard about some group or other patting themselves on the back and checking off an inclusivity box by adding an autistic person to an advisory board when the person doesn't have the abilities to absorb pertinent information and/or to add to substantive reform. That's not helping or including. That's exploitation!

Finally, let's take this advocacy discussion a bit deeper. There is some debate in the social media space about whether parents *should* participate in advocacy at all. A popular point keeps cropping up that autistic voices are the critical ones, not family members and caregivers. I fully agree that it's imperative to listen to autistic voices. But I also know sometimes you're going to have to talk to the families, not the autistic people themselves. Why? Pretty simple: some autistic people can't yet communicate their thoughts. If they can't do it, who will? They *need* others to speak up on their behalf! Denying participation to their parents erases these people's chance for any representation at all.

Chapter 20

And in the End

So back to bridges.

I hope that this book has built some for you. But where do we go from here?

I wanted to close some of the gaps between diagnostic language and daily life, between my experience of autism and that of my profoundly impacted peers, between the worlds of the neurotypical and the neurodivergent, between my 30-second social media reels and my in-depth analysis of autism issues. In finishing up the book I was never supposed to be able to write, one broad question remains for many readers: where do we go from here? I recommend a focus on the future.

I've spent more of my life dissecting the human experience than having one. Since adolescence, and even since childhood, I haven't enjoyed much of what people traditionally do to connect with each other. End result? When it comes to social interaction, I'm usually stuck on the outside. That's resulted in a lifetime of watching, observing, and (yes, I confess) analyzing and picking apart the social behaviors I witness. As I entered adolescence, I began to understand my autism diagnosis better, and also to have a fuller appreciation of how it affects relationships. Eventually I (mostly) accepted matters as they are, but the analysis continued. The habit ultimately led to my career in therapy. But it also sent me, however indirectly, through a surprising series of twists and turns to a level of autism advocacy I never dreamed I'd achieve—and valid advocacy demands I close this book by leaving you, also, focused on the future.

On whatever bridge you find yourself, please take a moment to consider what's ahead for all of us. Since the 1990s, the percentage of autistic people has climbed steadily upward. The CDC website statistics show an increase from 1 in 125 children to 1 in 36 children just in the last 20 years. However much anyone wants to argue about more *diagnosis* versus more actual *occurrence*, nobody can argue that's a really big change! Numbers are hardly my strong point, but even I can understand that kind of math.

Here's the thing: autism focus, autism funding, autism emphasis often stays on children. It's a natural tendency. Almost everyone wants children to have all possible advantages. And—as I emphasize to groups of therapists every month—all life's opportunities have an expiration date. The window will eventually close.

But understanding it pushes us toward another conclusion: the window of childhood is not the only one closing. With every turn of the calendar, more of yesteryear's little kids become adults. We all need to stop, think, and consider two things. First, those autistic people will continue to be adults a lot longer than they were children. Second, their parents are not getting any younger. And risking too much repetition, please, *please* remember: all those autistic people online bemoaning the difficulty of their jobs, their peer groups, their apartment hunting …? That's all valid. Very valid. It's also the minority of people who are affected by autism. A far greater percentage will never have the privilege of arguing online. They might never be able to work a job. They probably won't ever get to hunt for their own apartment. And they might never have any peer group. The most fortunate will have a sibling or other relative who'll assume the caregiver role when the parents can no longer do so. But what about the rest?

Each such person is an *individual* with hopes, goals, fears, and dreams. The people involved in this dilemma are your friends, your family, your loved ones. They might be you. They are me. Those individuals form a critical part of my long-term goals, so stand by for future books and future videos online.

From the onset, I've tried to emphasize that all topics in this book will forever have a dual perspective for me. I will always be both the autistic person and the one striving to help autistic people. I spend my life on bridges, forever begging for each group to understand another. Circumstances are urgent and growing by the day. It's hard to combine that urgency and good perspective without paralyzing everyone with dread. Yet that combination creates my sense of mission. And my challenge remains the same: look at the world with the filter of task breakdown. Life is made up of behaviors, so don't lose sight of the immense value of every individual step. What's in front of you today, right now, that you can do? What can you help with? Whose life can you improve, even for an hour?

Wherever you are, on or off the spectrum, and whatever gap you're trying to cross, remember that we can't build tomorrow's bridges until we understand today's barriers. I hope I've been able to increase your understanding at least a little. But your own proactive stance—focusing on small, specific, actionable steps—can become your most powerful weapon.

If you face something not addressed in this book, let me know about it. Put my name in the subject line and email *phfmedia@projecthopesc.org.* Suggestions matter, because if you're struggling with a certain problem, it's really unlikely you're the only one! Maybe somebody else is just as worried about a problem parallel to yours. Maybe we all need to look at it together? Let's gather as best we can in the center of the bridge and work to improve quality of life for all.

References

American Psychiatric Association: *Diagnostic and Statistical Manual of Mental Disorders,* Fifth Edition. Arlington, VA, American Psychiatric Association, 2013.

Debbaudt, Dennis, and Rothman, Darla: *Autism: Effective Resolutions, FBI Law Enforcement Bulletin* Volume: 70, Issue: 4. April 2001. Pages: 20-24. https://www.ojp.gov/ncjrs/virtual- library/abstracts/contact-individuals-autism-effective-resolutions

Hirvikoski, T., & Blomqvist, M. (2015). High self-perceived stress and poor coping in intellectually able adults with autism spectrum disorder. *Autism: the international journal of research and practice*, 19(6), 752–757. https://doi.org/10.1177/1362361314543530

Hughes MM, Shaw KA, DiRienzo M, et al. The Prevalence and Characteristics of Children With Profound Autism, 15 Sites, United States, 2000-2016. Public Health Reports®. 2023;138(6):971-980. doi:10.1177/00333549231163551

Lord, C., Chapman, D., Havdahl, A., et al.: "The *Lancet* Commission on the future of care and clinical research in autism," *The Lancet Commissions*. Volume: 399, Issue: 10321. January 2022. Pages 271-334. https://www.thelancet.com/journals/lancet/article/PIIS0140-6736(21)01541-5/

Trundle, G., Jones, K. A., Ropar, D., & Egan, V. (2023). Prevalence of Victimisation in Autistic Individuals: A Systematic Review and Meta-Analysis. *Trauma, Violence, & Abuse*, 24(4), 2282-2296. https://doi.org/10.1177/15248380221093689

Acknowledgments

My life carries a theme of irony in just about every possible way. I've already shared lots about the long series of apparent contradictions that led me to this moment—and to this book.

I find humor in my long list of ironic life truths. Others seem to find inspiration. I frequently hear how I've "beat the odds," and maybe I have. In my world, though, *my* inspiration for a person who "beat the odds" has always been my mother. Without her, I'd never have arrived at the place where I could write a book. When I was little, she'd tell me stories from her childhood that held darkness and struggle rather than irony. At the time I didn't really understand the intricacies of childhood abuse and neglect. All I knew was that, much like my favorite TV show and movie characters, Mom always emerged as the victor.

With my vivid imagination, I could always see in my mind what the characters in her stories might have looked like. The images of what could be considered her villains never scared me. I don't believe they really scared her either. She always described feeling a sense of empathy toward them, and maybe by default, I did too. I didn't need to comprehend the complexities of the alcoholism that killed my grandmother before I was born. I didn't need to understand all the complications resulting from poverty. Based on every other story my mother told me, two things became quickly evident. Mom was dealing with misfortune, not malevolence. And—as reliably as a Disney character—I always knew the story was going to end with her overcoming the adversity of the moment, no matter how unlikely.

This book physically manifests my own victories in a way initially thought to be out of reach, but my mom's physical scars can equally be considered evidence of triumph. If she could not only survive her circumstances but also go on to thrive in every area of her life … if she could be the first to break the family cycle of alcoholism, abuse, and poverty, surely I can do great things with the safe and loving childhood she provided to me. My story, and therefore this book, would never have existed without the love and dedication of my mother.

My story would not have been *written* if it weren't for the love and generosity of my Uncle Tommy. My mom's brother, Tommy, may not have emerged from his childhood as a victor exactly the same way Mom did, but he was a hero, nonetheless. His consistent acts of kindness and occasional mischief often played a huge role in my mom's ability to maintain her resilience as a little girl. In many of my mom's stories, Uncle Tommy was the hero who I knew would save the day. Fast-forward a generation, and he became a hero to another little girl: me.

Despite my loving home, autism and learning disabilities overwhelmed me and overshadowed much of our collective family life, even if we didn't yet know the correct terminology. Though still recovering from a terrible accident that left him unable to walk, Uncle Tommy funded the extensive academic and psychological testing that gave my parents a roadmap and signposts to help me move forward. Evaluations like that weren't any cheaper in 2007 than they are now. As difficult as the summary was for Mom to read, that big pile of paper opened the door for me to receive occupational therapy and specialized tutoring, leading the way to my involvement with Project Hope Foundation via a school for kids on the spectrum. Uncle Tommy gave me and my family a highly specialized gift of detailed information so we could better plan for my future.

Without my mom's love and resilience and Uncle Tommy's generous gift, I would not be where I am today, and this book would never have happened. I thank him for his generosity and concern and Mom for her courage to act on the results and use them to move me forward.

About the Publisher

PHF Media is a program of

Project HOPE Foundation
A Lifespan of Autism Services
www.projecthopesc.org

Project Hope Foundation is a South Carolina nonprofit started in 1997 by two moms of young sons with autism, Lisa Lane and Susan Sachs, who remain as Co-Executive Directors. In its 28th year of service, Project Hope Foundation's mission of providing a lifespan of autism services has led to expansion into nine campuses and four core programs: therapy, education, adult services and community engagement. These programs, serving over 1,000 annually, span across ages, from toddlers to adults, and across the levels and complexities of the autism spectrum.

Project Hope's therapy program currently serves nearly 300 children in Applied Behavior Analysis (ABA) therapy, along with in-house speech-language therapy and occupational therapy. In addition to daily therapy, Project Hope offers monthly meetings with each family to help generalize therapeutic gains into home and community life. Project Hope's education program consists of its own accredited school serving K5-12th grade, with three tiers of classrooms to meet needs across the spectrum. Additionally, staff provide support in over 30 local schools. Project Hope's adult program provides daily activities focused on building communication, increasing independence, and developing employment opportunities. As part of adult services, Project Hope developed an in-house digital customized shirt-printing business that allows adults to gain skills while earning paychecks. Project Hope's community engagement programs include trainings and presentations to a wide range of audiences, including families, educators, medical professionals, potential employers, and community civic groups.

Printed in Great Britain
by Amazon

53209431R00108